A get-well guidebook
to soothe the
body, mind & spirit

by Rebecca Rengo-Kocher MA, MSW, LCSW, ACSW

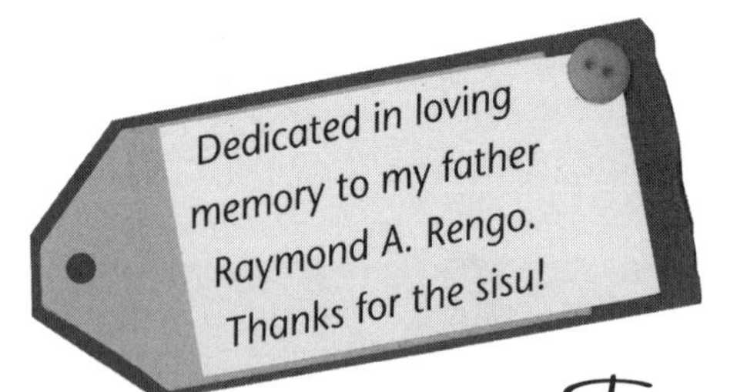

Introduction

In my 25 years as a geriatric social worker, psychotherapist and care manager, I have had many patients referred to me because they suffered with chronic pain.

I have counseled and consulted with people of varied ages, diagnoses, and in different settings—all trying to make it through each day.

My goal in writing this book is to help people who are hurting.

You are not alone. I do understand. I have suffered with chronic pain for more than 30 years, my entire adult life. I know what it is like to push myself with every ounce of my energy, right down to my soul... just to sit through a church service, a child's play time, a meeting.

I know what it's like when the pain is throbbing or it's aching or it's just there like a bruise that covers the entire body.

I know how it feels to be told by family, friends, even doctors and nurses that I should be feeling better, doing better. I know what it's like to be told I'm not trying hard enough, I am addicted to pain pills, that I complain too much ...or that I am a hypochondriac.

For many years, my pain was a 10, on a scale of one to 10. By following the techniques and advice in this guidebook, my pain is now usually a two.

I felt a calling to write this book, to share what has worked for me in the hope that it will be of some benefit to you.

The cornerstones of my struggle have been Hope, Faith, Perseverance and Love. These are the chapters of this book.

I have built my life on these strengths. I have emerged from the darkness, no longer swimming upstream. I have learned how to go with the flow of the current. I now can find, feel and express joy, happiness and pleasure.

Life is worth living. The body is not a prison; it is a temple to be honored and respected. You will have more and more good days once you learn this flow. You will have good days filled with joy.

Please do not give up hope. Do not throw your arms up in despair. It is hard but keep going. A life with chronic pain can be a life enjoyed and lived well.

I hurt with you and my heart feels for you. Come with me and let me be your guide through this book.

May God bless us all on this journey.

Acknowledgements:

This guidebook is the culmination of many experiences and many people's stories over the course of my adult life. I want to thank all of my clients who have shared their stories and experiences—you have touched me.

The actual names used in this book have been changed. Some people are a compilation of more than one person.

I deeply appreciate everyone who has helped me in my own healing journey. There are too many practitioners to thank everyone individually. So many of you have made a profound difference.

I do want to acknowledge Cindy Goodnetter who has not only treated me with massage and cranial sacral therapy for many years, but also referred me to most of the other practitioners I've used. Thank you for opening so many healing possibilities. You are an angel.

There are many friends and family who have provided so much emotional support for my healing. Thank you all. (Please also see Acknowledgements on page 95.)

Contents

Hope makes today possible
and tomorrow attractive,
or at least less threatening.
Hope is the mainstay of our energy.
We go forward — because we hope.

— Arthur Jones

You must grieve the loss of a "normal life." You are living a daily existence that is not what you would like it to be.

You need to be active in processing your grief. Grieving frees up hope, which is needed to move forward. You have lost what you used to be able to do. You also have to grieve the loss of what you wanted to do in the future but now can't plan to do. If you don't grieve through these feelings, you become "stuck." If you are stuck, you cannot live successfully with chronic pain.

Grieving is a complicated process. I have found the following steps most important in working on grief:

1. Accept your loss.
2. Process your anger, fear, sadness — toward your doctors, the pain, God, your family, yourself.
3. Make adjustments — physically, emotionally and environmentally.
4. Acknowledge your mood.
5. Come to terms with chronic pain.

The longer you take to start processing your grief, the longer you delay getting back to your life.

Healing Help

Arrange a time and place where you feel safe. Some people prefer to be alone while others feel more comfortable with a trusted friend or counselor. Facilitate your grieving by looking at pictures or magazines relating to your losses. Let your anger out! Don't' hold it back. The only way out of grieving is to go through it. It's painful, but you'll emerge stronger.

Do this at your own pace. Talking to a support person at some point facilitates the processing. You may repeat this several times or for several losses.

Family Support

You can't force someone to grieve. Allow them the space to be honest about how they are feeling. Don't try to cheer them up. Recognize and validate their feelings. "I believe your pain is real." "I understand it's very hard ....."

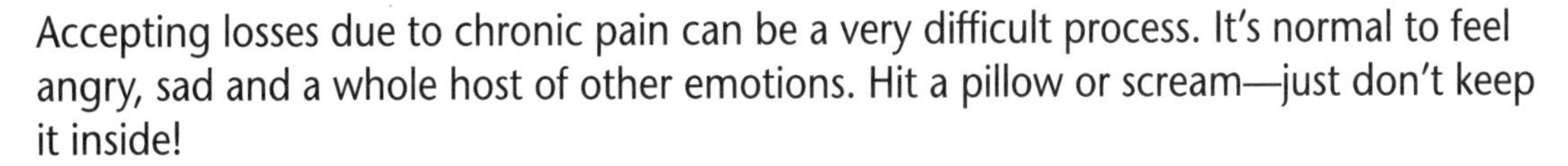

Exercise 1

Accepting losses due to chronic pain can be a very difficult process. It's normal to feel angry, sad and a whole host of other emotions. Hit a pillow or scream—just don't keep it inside!

List 10 losses you are now experiencing because of chronic pain. (They can be big, like losing your job, or smaller, like needing help from others to pick up packages.)

At first, it may be difficult to write. It's okay to put the list down and come back to it later. Keep trying to put your thoughts on paper.

1. ______________________________
2. ______________________________
3. ______________________________
4. ______________________________
5. ______________________________
6. ______________________________
7. ______________________________
8. ______________________________
9. ______________________________
10. ______________________________

What dreams have you had to change or modify because of your chronic pain? List five— they can be vacations you won't be able to go on or activities or goals you won't be able to continue with.

1. ______________________________
2. ______________________________
3. ______________________________
4. ______________________________
5. ______________________________

If you need to write more, feel free to do so on another piece of paper or write in the margins.

Exercise 2

Who are you mad at because of your chronic pain? Is it a family member that doesn't understand? A doctor whose intervention made it worse? God for not healing you? There are no right or wrong answers.

Name ___________________________

Relationship ________________________

Reason ____

____

Have you incorporated changes into your life because of the chronic pain? (It could be major, like structural changes to the house or even moving, to everyday changes, like not doing an activity that you know might aggravate your pain or following a new diet to feel better.) Write down what you're doing to make adjustments.

____

____

____

____

____

How do you feel about having chronic pain?

____

____

____

____

____

Are you able to be honest both with yourself and someone you trust, that you are feeling this way?

____

____

____

____

Grieving is hard work and it's a process that takes time. If you are feeling depressed or overwhelmed, seek professional support to help you through it. (See the Resources on page 92.)

To move forward with your life, your pain has to be at a functional level. This may not be a low level. We all have different thresholds of tolerance. If you cannot do what you need to do because the pain is too great, make it your priority to do whatever needs to be done to reduce the pain.

Your efforts to reduce pain must come before your children, your spouse, your job, your house and everything else. Once you have the pain at a manageable level, you can then work on reducing it more, at a slower pace, taking the rest of your life into account.

For the short term, enlist others to oversee the kids or help with the project at work — your priority is to function at a higher level.

Use pain medications and other acute treatments as a way to function while you research other options. Be vigilant about managing the pain. Effective pain management can be hard to find. Many doctors are not knowledgeable about pain management. They have many of the same myths and concerns that the public has. One common fear is addiction. It's important to know that addiction rarely occurs in patients who receive pain medications for a medical reason.

Physical dependence on pain medications is not addiction. People treated with some pain medications

Family Support

Chronic pain fluctuates. It's very common for someone to be able to do an activity at one time and later that day or the next day, not feel comfortable doing the same things. They are not doing this for attention or to be manipulative. Many factors come into play, other health problems aggravating the pain or fatigue, emotions, prior activity level and current level of pain, among others. Don't call this to their attention. Be understanding. Believe they want to do it.

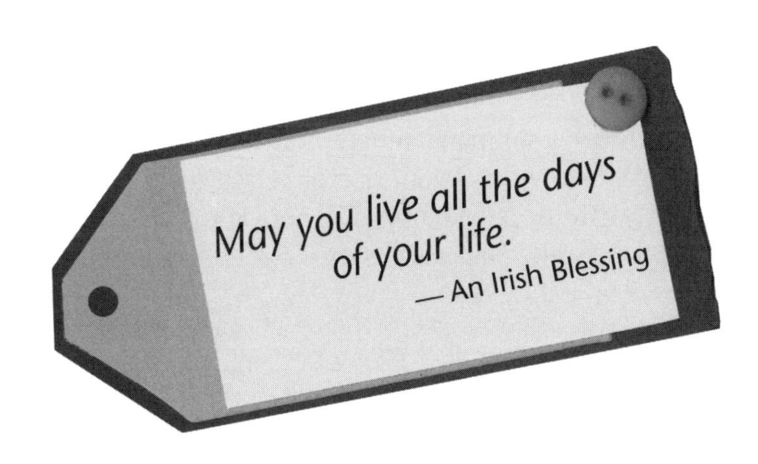

develop physical dependence and will experience withdrawal if they stop abruptly. Similar to someone taking medication for high blood pressure to better manage their health, a person with chronic pain may depend on pain pills to function. This is not an addition.

I'll never forget sitting in my pain management doctor's office and hearing his receptionist take phone calls canceling appointments because people hurt too much to come in. The pain will exist whether you stay in bed or go to the doctor; if you can get to the doctor, you may gain some relief. Staying in bed only delays what you need in this situation.

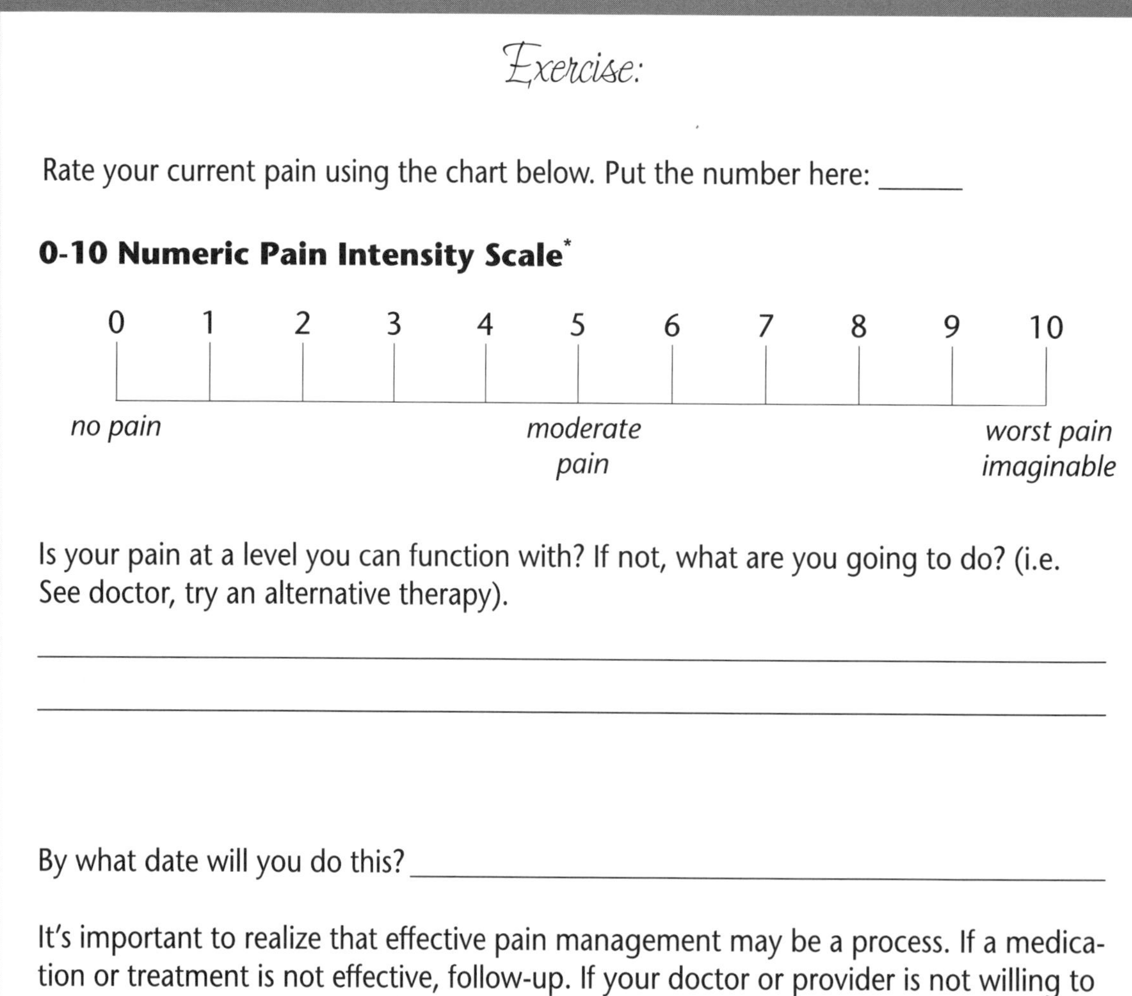

Exercise:

Rate your current pain using the chart below. Put the number here: ______

0-10 Numeric Pain Intensity Scale*

Is your pain at a level you can function with? If not, what are you going to do? (i.e. See doctor, try an alternative therapy).

____

____

By what date will you do this? ______________________________

It's important to realize that effective pain management may be a process. If a medication or treatment is not effective, follow-up. If your doctor or provider is not willing to try other options, get another doctor or provider who is more knowledgeable about pain management. There is always something else to try. Give each option appropriate time to work, but don't give up if it doesn't.

Repeat this exercise until your pain is at a level at which you can function.

Source: Acute Pain Management: Operative or Medical Procedures and Trauma, Clinical Practice Guideline No. 1. AHCPR Publication No. 92-0032: February 1992; Agency for Healthcare Research & Quality, Rockville, MD; pages 116-117.

Open your heart to the present moment, even if you don't like the moment. There is something to be gained from everything that happens — a lesson learned. Perhaps you'll approach situations differently or avoid certain ones. Looking at an incident from another perspective can also be enlightening.

Being open to different types of people, information and circumstances can facilitate learning and growth.

Many times we automatically shut our minds and hearts to whatever is going on in the present moment. Before shutting down, analyze why. Is it because it's different?

There are times when it is healthy for us to protect ourselves. But we should also periodically analyze our instinct for self-protection—we may be closing off new opportunities for growth out of fear.

I recently worked with a woman in her mid-30s named Lisa. She has chronic pain as a result of a bad car accident. Lisa has had surgeries and physical therapy, but her chronic pain continues. Her doctors don't understand why her pain is still so severe. They tell her there is not a medical explanation for it, and they don't know what else to do.

Lisa came to me reluctantly at her doctors' insistence. I encouraged her to try relaxation techniques; bio feedback; visualization; meditation; cognitive/behavioral techniques—the list goes on and on.

Family Support

Ask if your loved one wants to hear your views or suggestions before you start giving them. Be prepared to gracefully accept "no" or "not now." It's easy to think of ways someone should cope or adjust, but it's impossible to judge another person's pain. Show respect for their feelings.

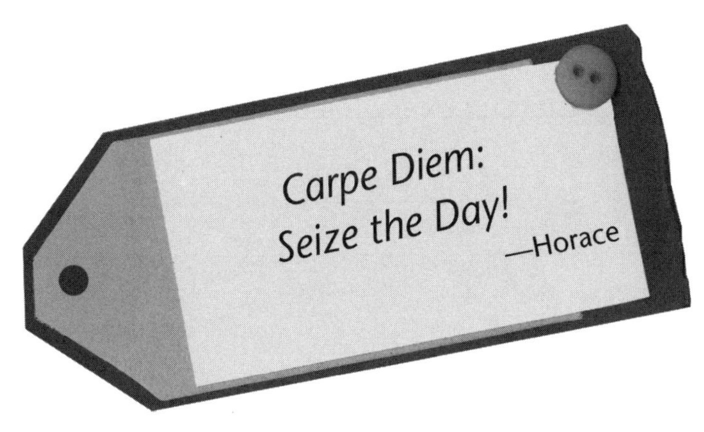

Lisa continually refused everything, stating she is not "new age." Lisa expected her doctors to cure her.

Lisa is missing out on so many opportunities for self-growth, as well as options that could help reduce her pain.

When I look back at my own journey with chronic pain, I see many benefits from almost everything I've tried, as well as the varied people I have met along the way. Meditation has helped me enjoy the moment and feel a closer connection with God. Visualization has helped me achieve health goals as well as personal and career goals. Cognitive/behavioral techniques have helped me change self-defeating patterns, helping not only my chronic pain, but my entire life.

Personally, I have experienced the most significant pain relief from alternative approaches like cranial sacral therapy, acupuncture and chiropractic subluxation. Not everything works equally for all people. It's worth the effort to try them and see what works for you.

I am so thankful I have tried and continue to implement many different approaches and that I have consulted with many different kinds of practitioners and professionals.

Different perspectives have broadened my own. Sincere caring and kindness from people so different from myself has touched me deeply. I am healing because of my open heart. My life is deeper and more meaningful as a result.

Whenever you can, open your heart to the present moment; it could be a healing moment you'll be glad you didn't miss.

Exercise

Name three things that you have learned or hope to learn from having chronic pain.

1. ______________________________

____

2. ______________________________

____

3. ______________________________

____

In order to stay open to all positive options in your life, practice being eclectic.

Listen to different kinds of music, change your radio dials in the car to different stations. Vary your routine from time to time. Eat new foods. Read authors or newspapers with opposing viewpoints.

Really listen to all kinds of people — children, the elderly, people from different economic classes, racial and ethnic or religious backgrounds. Wear something "just for fun."

Attend new events. Keep your mind open to everything, big and small—significant and insignificant.

Practice being non-judgmental. It takes a lot of energy, precious energy you don't want to waste, to maintain preconceived notions, prejudice or hatred.

Today, take a fresh look at the world. Answers to your healing may be right in front of you, waiting to be accepted.

Family Support

Do the same exercise as your loved one. Are you staying open minded? Don't push your own perspectives. It's the person's right to make their own decisions.

It's your right to set boundaries on what you will and won't do. Don't enable the person with chronic pain.

Exercise

Check everything you are doing to stay open-minded.

___ Listening to different music

___ Varying routine

___ Eating new foods

___ Going to a restaurant that you haven't tried

___ Attending different cultural festivals

___ Reading books or publications that are different from your own perspective

___ Attending religious services or ceremonies different from your own

___ Wearing something fun or out of the ordinary

___ Volunteering at a nursing home, a headstart program or soup kitchen

___ Listening to different people; while volunteering, riding the bus, visiting an elderly person or playing with a child. This literally means that you encourage them to talk, and you just listen without much talking.

___ Learning to meditate or do yoga

___ Just sitting and watching the sunset or children playing

Others:

____

____

____

____

Believe you are worthy of pleasure and happiness right now. You do not have to wait for the pain to become better or go away. Enjoy your life now. If your pain is too severe to enjoy life the way you want to, find new ways to feel pleasure. If you can no longer run in the park, walk or go in your wheelchair. If you can't write or read because of your hands or eyes, use your ears to listen. Appreciate the simple things whenever you can.

I am often grateful I can no longer rush through life. My pain and health have slowed me down. I will always remember going on a field trip to the art museum with my youngest son's second-grade class. I had promised to go for weeks. I had turned in my chaperone form to the teacher and was scheduled. That morning I had an excruciating headache. My pain was so intense I didn't want to go. My son was so excited and proud I was going that I couldn't turn back. I enjoyed the exhibit on angels from the Vatican. I enjoyed eating a picnic on the grass outside with my son and his friends. I will always treasure the special moments I had with my child that day. I remember the beauty and the love. I don't remember my headache.

The world is full of beauty to be enjoyed. I am worthy of the pleasure these blessings can bring. Sometimes I am experiencing these moments because of my pain and not in spite of it.

Family Support

Give the person permission to enjoy themselves. Many people feel guilty when they have chronic pain and punish themselves (often subconsciously) by not having any pleasure. Encourage them with empathy.

Exercise

What are you doing to enjoy your life right now?

Practice doing something special for yourself every day. Choose from the list below and add your own ideas. Write down what you will do each day, until you have incorporated it as part of your daily routine; usually this takes 30 days.

___ Read a good book
___ Read a newspaper
___ Read magazines

___ Go on outings
___ Go to the movies
___ Go on drives
___ Go to the country
___ Go to a favorite park
___ Go out to eat

___ Take a long bubble bath
    ___ with candles
    ___ playing soft music
    ___ burning incense

___ Visit with friends
___ Talk on the phone with friends

___ Eat a special treat, like chocolate or ice cream

___ Buy yourself a small present
___ Buy yourself a big present

___ Get a massage
___ Get a manicure
___ Get a pedicure
___ Get a facial

___ Try alternative therapies like:
    ___ Acupuncture
    ___ Energy work
    ___ Cranial sacral therapy

Others:

____

____

____

____

____

Plan each day in advance to ensure something special happens.

Monday: ________________________
____

Tuesday: ________________________
____

Wednesday: ______________________
____

Thursday: _______________________
____

Friday: _________________________
____

Saturday: _______________________
____

Sunday: _________________________
____

Not everyone is an optimist or has a good sense of humor. I did not have either quality when I was young. I learned to develop these qualities. I don't try to be something I'm not. I read books, tape positive affirmations on my mirror and spend time with people who are optimistic and/or have a good sense of humor. I've found many people have one without the other; many people also have both.

Developing a sense of humor has been a powerful tool in my healing. I meet with a girlfriend regularly to go to the movies, almost always a comedy. I read the comics every morning. I enjoy joking with friends. I search out ways to have fun.

I have found being more optimistic and having a good sense of humor support each other.

I visualize positive changes happening. I see this book being published and helping others. I see myself sitting next to Oprah!

I visualize myself better every day. Often, I see myself laughing and happy.

Your mind is a powerful tool. Use it for change.

Family Support

You are not responsible for or capable of curing your loved one. Remain optimistic yourself. Be sure to have fun regularly. Don't let your life become sullen because someone you care about is hurting. The better you feel, the more you can support them.

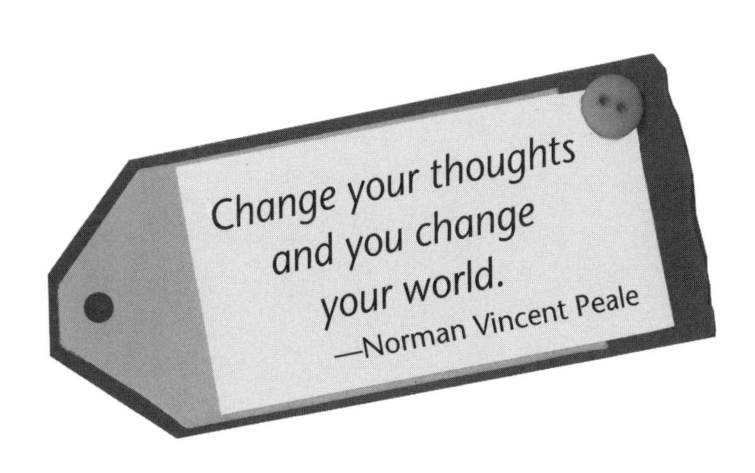

Exercise

What do you want to believe about yourself? Choose from the positive affirmations on the last page of this book (cut out slips) and put them wherever you will see them throughout your day—on your bedroom and bathroom mirror, refrigerator, briefcase, desk.

The more you see and read the same thought, the faster it will incorporate into your mindset. Do this consistently for at least 30 days. Add your own affirmations. This will facilitate an amazing mental shift for you.

Affirmations:

I am coping.

I am happy.

I am strong.

I am healthy.

I am healing.

I am positive.

I am fun.

I am content.

I am full of energy.

I am doing a good job.

I am a good person.

I am kind.

I am patient.

I am caring.

Michael J. Losier in *Law of Attraction,* recommends using the expression, "I'm in the process…" or "I've decided…" in front of the positive affirmation. You may want to add these prefixes if they help you believe the affirmations. Michael Losier also recommends telling yourself "lots can happen" to support a mental shift.

One of the lessons I keep learning over and over is that healing takes time.

I have to allow myself the time to heal. If I am tired after a treatment, I need to lie down. I can choose to push through my fatigue, but eventually this method catches up with me, and I will crash.

When I have a cold or an off day, I can choose to rest more. I consciously have to work at healing. I have to listen to my body and honor what it needs.

I need to rest when I am tired, eat when I am hungry, and do what my body needs to maintain and heal. This is one of the hardest lessons for me to integrate.

In the moment I want to push myself. For the long-term I need to give myself time to heal.

Family Support

If you see your loved one seemingly not doing anything, leave them alone. You may be thinking, "I leave them alone on their bad days. When they're feeling better they should help."

In order to increase their overall well being, they need to pace themselves every day, especially on the good ones, in order to avoid a relapse.

If you feel taken advantage of, consider counseling to help you establish appropriate boundaries and options for yourself.

Exercise 1

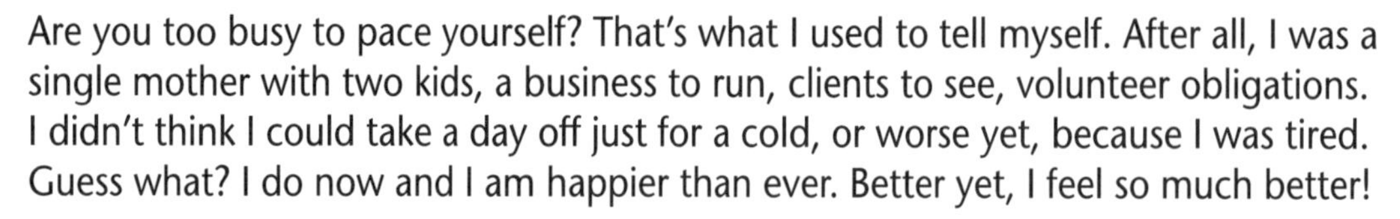

Are you too busy to pace yourself? That's what I used to tell myself. After all, I was a single mother with two kids, a business to run, clients to see, volunteer obligations. I didn't think I could take a day off just for a cold, or worse yet, because I was tired. Guess what? I do now and I am happier than ever. Better yet, I feel so much better!

Start with one day. What one activity can you eliminate or put off? Start small… is it not cleaning a room, saying "no" to a volunteer request, saying "no" to your kids? No matter what it is, take that time for yourself—read, sit outside, whatever. Whether it's five minutes or an hour, give it to yourself.

The next day, do the same thing. And the next day, do the same thing. Write down what you plan to eliminate this week:

____

____

____

____

____

Exercise 2

You are mastering the art of taking care of yourself. In the previous exercise, you are eliminating or refusing to add an activity.

Now, for the life-changing part—underschedule.

When you plan your day or week, give yourself lots of cushion time. If it takes half an hour to drive to an appointment, give yourself 45 minutes. You can even schedule blank time! That way if there is a traffic jam, the kids have an incident that requires your attention, or you are in a meeting that goes too long, you are okay.

No stress, no worry.

Use the extra time for yourself! Meditate, pray, relax. Approach life more gently at a slower pace. You'll enjoy life more because you will have less pain.

Religion is a deeply personal issue. Many people believe God will heal them and that they don't need to do anything on their own to facilitate the healing process.

Others are angry with God for not preventing their pain. I don't believe God causes our pain and suffering. Sometimes it's random, other times it's from poor judgment, bad luck or timing.

I believe one of the purposes of religion and believing in a spiritual power is not to make our lives better or easier, but to give us hope. Faith in a higher power gives hope. Surrendering to a higher power gives hope. Belief in a spiritual presence in our lives provides a sense of inner peace.

I don't blame God for my pain. I pray for healing, but I don't expect God to heal me without effort on my part. I do believe God gives me grace, inner peace and one of the most blessed gifts of all: *HOPE*.

Family Support

Read *When Bad Things Happen to Good People* by Rabbi Harold Kushner.

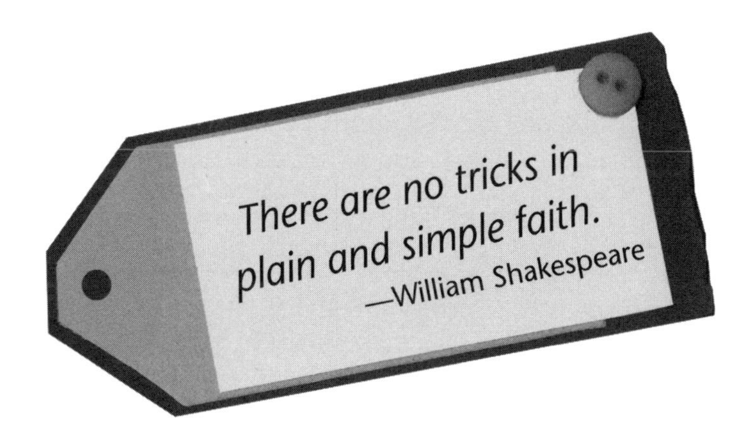

Exercise

Write down your own prayer for healing and say it daily. I heard a line from a prayer that resonated with me—*Heal me, change me, strengthen me—in body, mind, soul and spirit.*

I don't know the whole prayer, but I have borrowed these lines and incorporated them into my daily prayers for the last few years. The result is that I am healing, changing and becoming stronger in mind, body, soul and spirit.

Write your prayer below:

Write down your thoughts below, honestly and unedited:

How do you feel about God?

How do you feel about religion?

Do you blame God for your pain?

What do you hope for?

We are travelers on a cosmic journey — stardust, swirling and dancing in the eddies and whirlpools of infinity. Life is eternal. But the expressions of life are ephemeral, momentary, transient.

— *Deepak Chopra*

Healing Help

Schedule time to practice your faith. Whether formally or informally, structured or loose, be sure to allow the needed time and space.

It may be praying, reading, walking or attending a service every morning or once a week. It may be writing, talking with others one-on-one or participating in discussion groups.

Include faith as a part of your daily schedule so you won't forget. The consistency of practicing faith is a great comfort.

Family Support

In discussing faith, be aware not to push your own viewpoint on your loved one.

Ask how they feel. Don't assume. Respect whatever their feelings are. Faith is a very personal decision. I know people of different religions who attend services for the social aspects and because it's expected, but the concepts aren't meaningful. I've talked with others who are deeply spiritual but never attend a service.

You have to put effort into having and keeping faith.

If you believe in a spiritual presence in your life, you can have moments of peace and comfort even in the midst of severe pain.

Many people have become disillusioned with organized religion. But religion can be a bridge to spirituality. I believe that spiritual energy, universal energy and God are different ways of expressing the same presence. Varying religions are different bridges to the same essence.

What do you believe? Do you feel more comfortable following an organized religion or is walking in the woods your worship service?

Some people have been hurt by religion. Please don't let this keep you from feeling the inner peace and surrender that can make this painful existence more bearable and make the good times more meaningful. In whatever way you feel comfortable, work on your faith. It's a blessing we can all develop.

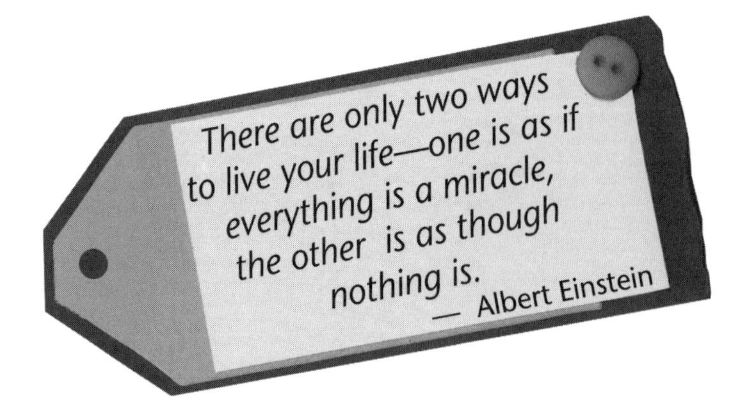

Exercise

What do you believe? ______________________________

____

____

____

How do you define God? ______________________________

____

____

Write out any thoughts or words that come to mind.

____

____

____

Are you comfortable with your beliefs?

____

____

Do you experience conflict with others about your beliefs? If yes, how do you handle that conflict?

____

____

____

How do your beliefs give you strength (i.e. services, reading literature, prayer)?

____

____

____

How can your beliefs and strengths help you cope at this time?

____

____

____

Many people with chronic pain feel guilty. I did. "I must have done something." "If I were really a good person this would not be happening to me." "Is God punishing me for a past sin?" "Am I just weak?" "If I tried harder, did more, would this pain exist?" "Am I being selfish?" "I feel guilty." "I feel sorry for myself." "I feel guilty that others are in worse shape." "I feel guilty that I hurt."

Recently, I worked with Bertha, a 95-year-old woman with severe fibromyalgia. She received this diagnosis about three years ago. One year after diagnosis, she was in a car accident. After rehab, she has been in a nursing home trying to improve to the point where she can go home and take care of herself.

Bertha was very critical of herself. She was disgusted with herself for not improving. She felt guilty that she was not doing everything for herself. She felt she still had to manage all her own financial affairs even though this stressed her.

The more she pushed herself physically and beat herself up emotionally, the worse her pain became.

Now, Bertha is in the process of letting go of her guilt. She is increasingly accepting her health, her pain and her limitations. She is learning to be easier on herself. She doesn't feel guilty or responsible for everything. She knows that many things are out of her control. She says the Serenity Prayer daily. She is surrendering to her faith. She is finding the positive in herself and her circumstances.

When I meet with Bertha now, she smiles and jokes. When she has a flare-up, she accepts that she can't do as much. When she is doing better, she is fully enjoying every moment.

Bertha tells me she is still working on letting go of her guilt. It's a process. I see so much progress already. Her condition hasn't changed but she has and will continue to do so.

Guilt is destructive. Guilt weighs down the spirit. Guilt stands in the way of progress. Let go of guilt.

Healing Help

Louise L. Hay has several books with beautiful prayers and affirmations. Spend a few hours looking through her books and find the affirmations or prayers that resonate within you. Post these affirmations wherever you will see and read them throughout the day—on mirrors, wallets, refrigerators. Place a prayer or journal by your bed to remind you to say it or write in it every morning and night. Submerge yourself in the positive. If done consistently, this really works.

Be aware of what you say and how you say it to your loved one. Be careful about telling someone what to do. You really don't know how they feel or how much they hurt.

Well-meaning friends and family often perpetuate guilt by telling people they should be doing certain things or feeling certain ways. Accept your loved one and focus on the positives, however far and few between they may be at times.

Exercise

1. Do you often feel guilty or responsible for your chronic pain? If yes, do you know why?

   ____

   ____

2. Do you feel guilty or responsible for other people? If so, for whom and why?

   ____

   ____

3. Write down which things in question #1 and #2 are in your control.

   ____

   ____

   ____

4. If there are things within your control in #3, write down what you can do to rectify or resolve them.

   ____

   ____

5. Now, write down what you can't control.

   ____

   ____

6. Are you willing to surrender the things you can't control in #5? If you are, write out how you will work on surrendering or letting go (prayer, rituals like writing the items on paper, posting affirmations, etc.).

   ____

   ____

7. If there are multiple items in #6 , pick the top priority to work on first. Repeat your plan every day for 30 days. Whether you are praying, saying affirmations or writing, do it as positively as you can. At the end of 30 days, you will feel a sense of relief. Move on to the next item in the same way.

Healing Help

Let others know you are grateful for them, whether it's big or small. Share your gratitude. Tell your family every day what you appreciate about them. Do they have a good sense of humor? Did they make your coffee in the morning? Share anything and everything.

Tell the receptionist in the doctor's office you appreciate her help. Tell the grocery store clerk she has a pretty necklace. Say whatever you appreciate to everyone you can whenever you can. Soon your day will be full of gratitude.

Practice gratitude. I start and end every day thankful for the blessings in my life. There have been many times I have had to struggle to come up with positives to appreciate. Did I have enough to eat? To pay bills (or at least make payments)? Clothes to wear?

Be thankful for anything and everything related to your life as a whole. If your pain was better in some way, say thank you. If it was a deplorable day, be grateful that you survived it. Don't ignore issues with your pain, but use time each day to appreciate what you can. Your pain may be so intense and depressing, the only positives may seem totally separate from you. Did you view a pretty sunset? Children laughing? Did you enjoy a tasty treat? A friend's voice? Be grateful.

I will never forget an elderly lady I visited in the nursing home. She was very ill and had severe chronic pain. She needed two people to help her move from her bed to a chair in her room, and once she was in the chair she was left to sit indefinitely. Her eyesight was rapidly declining and she was legally blind. She cheerfully made rugs to sell to raise money for a grandson who suffered brain damage during a violent assault. I felt tears come to my eyes when she told me with a smile, "I am so grateful these patterns have such big holes so I can feel where to go."

Say thank you to God, to the universe or write it down in a journal. Just express your appreciation for good things. You'll feel better inside. The more you practice gratitude, the more there is to be grateful for.

Tell your loved one what you appreciate about them and about others. A positive attitude is catching.

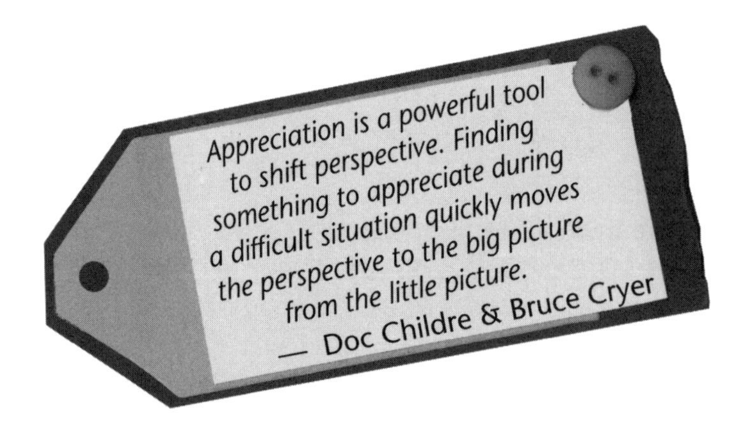

Exercise

Every day, either write in a journal or say in a prayer three things you are grateful for. Do not skip a day. It only takes a few minutes and the rewards are enormous. Start looking for the positives in everything. See benefits where you didn't before. It transforms the cynical to the appreciative. It's magical!

Begin right now by listing three things:

You have to work hard for whatever you want or need more of in your life. To feel better with pain, you must make this a top priority in your life. Not after you come home from work, after the kids are fed, the house is cleaned and the bills are paid. All of these things and others are important, but you need to be your own first priority.

That doesn't mean you neglect your responsibilities or other people. It means that you change your mindset about how you approach things.

I thought to be a good mother I always had to put my children first. Of course, there have been times I was in bed or the hospital or just too full of pain to function adequately. I only took care of myself when I felt too bad to move.

When I changed my approach and, more importantly, my frame of mind, not only did my health improve and my pain decrease, but I felt good about the way I handled my job as a mother. I didn't wait until I was nonfunctional to find time to rest. I paced myself. I took steps like getting a massage before my pain was too severe to move.

There are times when my kids want my attention and I can give it. Other times I explain to them I need to rest first or do something else to take care of myself. When I feel better overall, I am better able to cope with their needs.

Take care of yourself first and the rest of your life will follow suit.

Healing Help

It's hard for many people, especially women, to do nice things for themselves. Many women tell me they feel selfish. In reality, it's selfish *not* to. If you feel sick, have pain flare-ups or are unhappy, you negatively impact everyone around you. It's your responsibility to take care of yourself, physically and emotionally, so you can share what's best about you with others.

Plan to do something nice for yourself every day for the next 30 days. If you don't plan it, you won't have time. Whether it's a medical appointment, getting your hair done or quiet time alone—schedule it!

Family Support

Are you taking care of yourself? You are a caregiver, either physically or emotionally. Make yourself your own first priority. Follow the same exercises as those for the person with chronic pain. Don't let yourself become run down, depressed or develop chronic health or pain problems. Be a good role model. Do something nice for yourself every day.

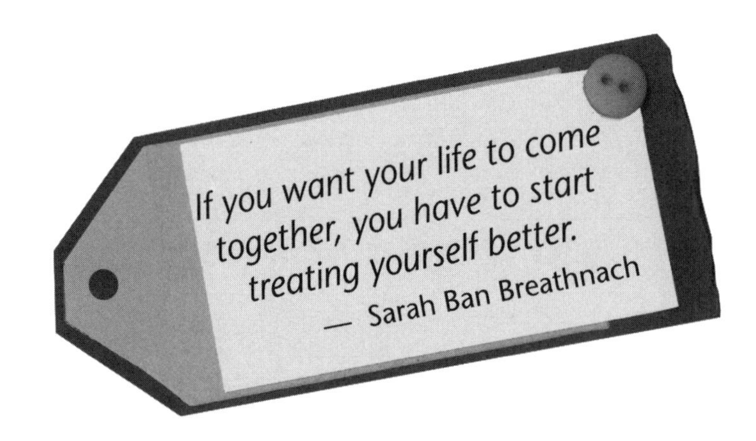

Exercise

1. Are you able to make yourself a top priority every day? If not, why not?

____

____

____

____

2. What do you do or can you do to make your health and yourself a top priority?

____

____

____

____

3. In the next week, write one thing you plan to do for yourself every day:

Sunday: _______________________________________

Monday: _______________________________________

Tuesday: _______________________________________

Wednesday: _____________________________________

Thursday: ______________________________________

Friday: ____

Saturday: ______________________________________

Relax! As hard as this is when you are hurting, it is the best thing you can do. When you are in pain and you fight against it, you become more anxious and add to your pain. Breathe deeply. Listen to soft music. Meditate. Pray. Get a massage. Talk on the phone. Do whatever is within your power to help you relax. Find professionals who believe you, get the best medications or treatments, and practice relaxing.

When you have a good day, pace yourself and take care of yourself. I used to push myself too hard to catch up on things when I was having a good day. Often after a good day, I would collapse or consequently have several bad days. I would then feel depressed and start obsessing that I would never have another good day. I would focus on my fear that the last good day really was my last and gradually I would become more depressed. Eventually I would start to feel better and then on a "good day" I would overextend myself again and the cycle would be repeated.

Now I take care of myself on good days, too. I pace myself, gradually doing more over a period of good days instead of all on one day. Now, when I overextend myself or have a bad day or days, I am gentle with myself. I remind myself what I need to do and that better days will come. I encourage myself to be grateful and not to panic. I tell myself this is not a permanent decline but a temporary backslide. Better days are ahead.

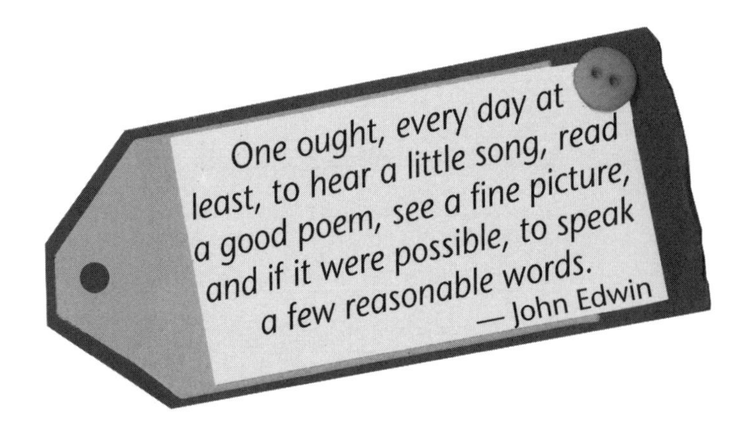

Healing Help

Underschedule your time. If you think a work project will take three hours to complete, then schedule three-and-a-half or four hours. If you finish and don't need a break, you can be ahead of schedule. If you do need to go slower, rest or regroup, you can do so without stress.

Use this at home, too. If you are picking up the kids and it takes 15 minutes to get there, give yourself 30. If traffic is bad or you need extra time, you aren't stressed. If you get there early, relax!

Pacing is very important for people with chronic pain. It's often hard for people without pain to understand this. They may seem fine and what they want help with may not seem like much to you. However, if a person is hurting and/or has fatigue, simple things can take a lot of effort.

Encourage your loved one to pace their activities and rest. Be understanding that something simple, like a bath, can take a lot out of someone. Your loved one will function better overall with consistent pacing.

Exercise

1. It's difficult to relax when you are in pain. If you regularly practice relaxing, you will incorporate pacing into your day. Flare-ups may decrease and you will be better equipped to relax when needed for pain control. How do you practice relaxing? (You can use visualization, breathing, tapes, music, meditation, etc.)

   ____

   ____

   ____

2. Do you feel comfortable with your technique? If not, practice regularly until you do.

   ____

3. Do you pace yourself? Have you thought through what pace works best? Some people like structured time schedules, others are more flexible; be sure you schedule time to relax along with your other activities. Listen to what your body needs. Don't judge yourself negatively if you need a nap. Do what works best for you.

   ____

4. Meditation has changed my life. It's easier than you may think to meditate. Even if you devote only five minutes a day, please practice it daily. Below are the simple steps to follow:

   - ☐ Find a quiet place. I prefer complete silence, but a lot of people like soft background music. Sit comfortably with your back straight.
   - ☐ Place your palms facing up in your lap.
   - ☐ Close your eyes. Think of a word, like *healing*, or focus on breathing slowly in and out.
   - ☐ Breathe deeply in through your nose. Fill your abdomen so that it extends. Slowly bring your breath up into your chest expanding it with air. Exhale slowly through your mouth.

   If thoughts come into your head, just observe them as a witness. Let them come and go easily. Do not try to force them out. It's part of the process. The more you meditate, the easier it will become for your mind to relax. When your mind is relaxed, your body is relaxed.

Always have something to look forward to. Whether it's a vacation, a weekly phone call with someone special or private time set aside just for you, make it your job to keep a sparkle in your life. Anticipate something special every day.

When it's sunny outside, I look forward to a few minutes of feeling the sun on my face. I schedule time alone each week with my kids. I keep things flexible. Sometimes we just hang out and talk or watch a game on TV. We might play a board game, go out to eat or see a movie. It depends on my energy level and mood and their's.

I talk with my mother at least once a week on the phone. I used to fold laundry when we talked. Now I sit back and give all of my attention to her and to our phone call. I enjoy it so much more. I look forward to that time to simply relax and cherish my mother.

My very first client, Charlie, will forever touch me. Charlie was blind and had numerous aches and ailments. His wife, Ethel, had problems with her hip, which limited her walking, but overall she enjoyed good health. I would see them one to two times a week. I would visit with Ethel and then take Charlie out to do banking, grocery shopping and errands.

Ethel complained constantly and was miserable. She had visitors and phone calls. Charlie did the cooking and most of the household chores. Ethel watched TV. Charlie always had a smile on his face. He would tell me he looked forward to going out all week. He was so appreciative of clerks in the store who would help him.

He anticipated sunny days, friendly exchanges with strangers and making something new for a meal. He looked forward to the smallest things and relished them. Charlie always found the sparkle.

You, too, can find ways to create joy in your life every day. It's up to you to find the sparkle.

Healing Help

Create a wish box. Decorate it with magazine pictures of activities, things or people that you want more of in your life.

Write down three specific things you would like to have in your life that you don't have now. Is it a vacation somewhere, a mate, energy to do certain things? Don't limit yourself. It's your wish box. Update it every year.

Family Support

Encourage your loved one to have dreams and goals. Don't tell them something isn't possible. Who knows?

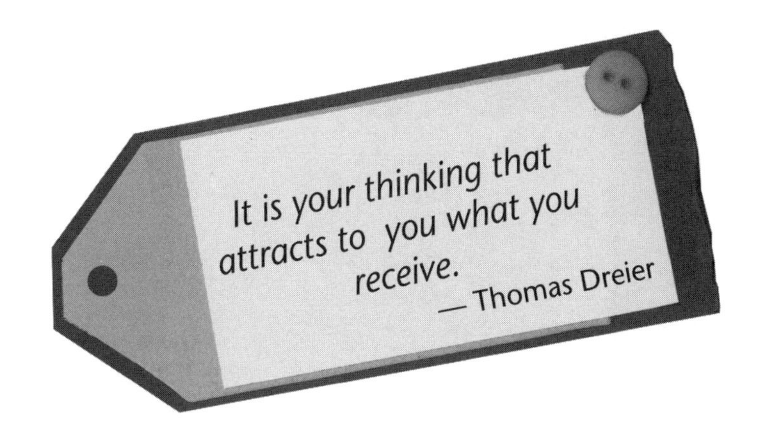

Exercise

1. What do you look forward to? Do you have something each day, even if it's small? If not, start now. Write out everything you can think of that you look forward to (I.e. meeting a friend for lunch, curling up in a favorite chair with a book, soaking your feet, taking a class):

____
____
____
____
____
____
____
____
____

2. What can you create or add to your life to give it more sparkle? Do you need to spend more time with family or friends, go out more, treat yourself to fresh flowers, get a massage or something else? It's important to do something special on a daily basis.

____
____
____
____
____
____
____
____

Healing Help

Tell yourself you forgive someone, even if you don't. Say it over and over to yourself several times a day. Tape up affirmations that reinforce you are a forgiving person. Pray for strength and grace to forgive. Surrender the issue to your faith. When you are ready, pray for the person; they need it. Pray for yourself; you need it.

You don't have to wait to feel forgiveness to practice it. Often, the opposite is true. If you practice forgiveness, you will start to feel it. It feels good!

Forgive friends, family, clergy and doctors—anyone who has in any way caused, aggravated or misunderstood your pain.

You also have a role in your pain. When you hold on to your anger toward others, you are holding on to your pain. You make choices every day. Some choices may have been the wrong ones. Forgive yourself. Let go. You did the best you could at the time. You know better now. You are wiser now. Learn the lessons and move on.

Tell others you forgive them. Pray for strength to forgive. Look at yourself in the mirror and tell your reflection that you forgive yourself.

Hurt and anger, like other emotions, are similar to the layers of an onion: realize that you can forgive at one level, and then, when more layers are peeled away, you may find the strength to forgive more.

Forgiveness equals letting go and does not imply that what happened was okay or even that you are going to have anything to do with the person you are forgiving. It means you are not going to waste any more energy on this issue.

Each time you work on forgiving and are truly able to let go, you are closer to healing. When you forgive, you give the gift of peace to yourself. It is a healing gift.

Be aware of your boundaries. You may hold others responsible for things that your loved one doesn't and vice versa. Everyone has a different perspective. Don't judge differences.

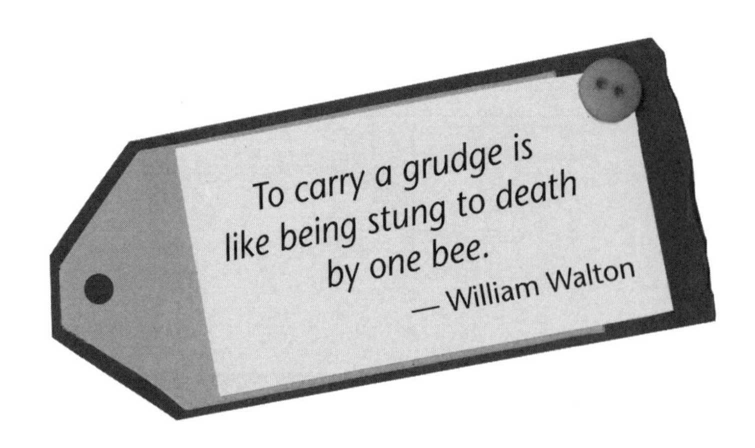

Exercise

1. List everyone you are angry with or have been hurt by:

2. Have you forgiven everyone? If not, do you know what is keeping you from forgiving? Sometimes it's a fear that if we forgive, they will hurt us again. Can you pinpoint your block with forgiving each person?

3. Once you identify why you are not forgiving someone, can you identify a flaw in your reasoning? If it's to punish someone, the reality is you are hurting yourself.

Healing Help

If you are taking longer than you thought you should to reach your goal, readjust your expectations. Be patient with yourself. Get feedback from trusted professionals as to whether or not you are being realistic. Remember slow and steady is better than fast and crash.

Recovery takes a long time, often much longer than we want to wait. We want the pain to end right now. If we work at being healthy every day, the changes may seem so incremental we don't notice. One day we think back and remember that one year ago, or ten years ago, it was worse. We still want it to be better. We need to keep practicing being healthy and have faith that one year from now we'll feel better.

My elderly aunt was a geriatric nurse. She shared books on gerontology with me and encouraged my interest in working with the elderly. For 10 years she has been in a wheelchair suffering numerous aches and pains. She quickly forgot words of advice and direction she used to give her patients. Her situation seemed hopeless to her and she slowly deteriorated. Her husband unexpectedly died and at 80 years of age she was moved into a nursing home.

Then she shifted her thinking. She became determined to move out of the nursing home. That was not how she planned to live out her life. With physical therapy and patience she slowly started walking again. She put everything she had into small accomplishments, she persevered day in and day out. She knew she had to be able to take care of herself in order to move out.

After eight months, she was able to move into her own apartment. For 10 years she had felt too bad to try, and she had become worse and depressed. In only eight months she was functioning and happy to be on her own again. Practice patience while you work on being healthy.

Family Support

Support your loved one in their goal. Remember it's their goal, not yours. Don't take responsibility for whether they are adhering to their plan. They need full ownership in order to be committed.

> Never become irritable waiting for things to get better. If you'll be patient, you'll find that you can wait much faster.
> — Unknown

Exercise

1. Do you have a goal that you are working toward? Write down your goal as specifically as you can. For example, my aunt wanted to move into a senior retirement apartment. What's yours?

2. In order to reach a goal, there are objectives or action steps that need to be accomplished. My aunt knew that in order to move, she would have to be able to handle her own personal care. She knew that would involve standing independently, walking short distances, transferring herself, and doing her own hygiene care and dressing/undressing. My aunt had to do strengthening exercises, gradually building her endurance and muscle tone. She also had to learn how to use adaptive devices to help herself with dressing and undressing. She started out small and slowly added to her accomplishments. What action steps do you need to take to reach your goal?

Healing Help

The more objectively you can look at yourself and your situation, the easier it is to cope with. When you are having a hard time, pretend you are talking to your best friend about the situation and how to handle it. Be as positive and encouraging in your self-talk as you would if you were your best friend.

There were times in my life that I survived chronic pain because I separated myself from it as objectively as I could. I told myself there was a reason I was suffering beyond my threshold. I read books to find the reason. I prayed. I told myself my soul was growing. I thought there were spiritual reasons I didn't understand.

I have faith that there are many things I don't understand. I gave up trying to find the right answer to why my suffering was so intense. There were periods I observed the pain, as if it were happening to someone else. I told myself that perhaps there would be a reason and it would become apparent to me later. When I decided to write this book, I looked at the days that were extremely painful as background material for me to use in helping others. Above all, I focused on making it through by the grace of God.

When you look for positive meaning or purpose in your pain, it helps lessen the negative impact. Does the pain help you appreciate others and value relationships? Perhaps you are developing problem-solving skills, character and becoming stronger emotionally.

There aren't always answers to every question. Faith helps me accept not knowing. Pray to make it by the grace of God.

Family Support

Resist the temptation to tell your loved one what positives you think they've gained from their health and pain issues. Tell them only if they ask. It can feel like you are minimizing their feelings if you point out their gains when they aren't yet ready to hear them. It can actually create a wall between you. That is not positive for anyone.

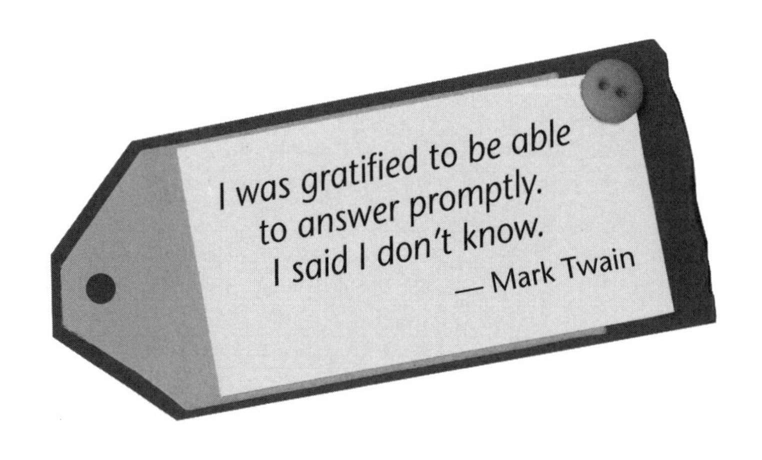

Exercise

What positive meaning or purpose has resulted because of the pain you experience?

Press on—nothing in the world
can take the place of persistence.
Talent will not—nothing is more common
than unsuccessful people with talent.
Genius will not—unrewarded genius is almost a
proverb. Education will not—the world
is full of educated derelicts. Persistence
and determination alone are omnipotent.

— Calvin Coolidge

Healing Help

If you resist something, it becomes more entrenched; when you accept something, you release its hold.

Family Support

Recognize that your loved one will have intense emotions. These feelings should pass. If they don't, encourage them to talk to a doctor about their feelings. If they are suffering from depression and/or anxiety, advocate for them to receive appropriate treatment, both medication and talk therapy. When someone is clinically depressed or anxious, they need help and support to overcome it. In that situation, it is hard for them to advocate for themselves.

Accept whatever feelings you may be having. Do not fight against feelings you do not wish to be experiencing. Observe them as objectively as possible. Think to yourself, "I am feeling very angry or disappointed or apathetic" — in time your feelings will change. Be hopeful that the next feeling will be more pleasant or better. Detach as much as you can.

Gayle is a good example of someone who hasn't detached. She is an attractive, married, middle-aged woman with two grown children and four grandchildren. She frequently has abdominal pain first thing in the morning. It subsides after she is awake for awhile and is normally gone by lunchtime. Her husband has taken her to numerous specialists. She has tried many different treatments, procedures and medications, but the pain remains unchanged.

Gayle is able to function pretty well with her condition. She volunteers at a charity gift shop, is active in her church and goes out dancing every Saturday night with her husband. Gayle's biggest issue is her obsession with her feelings and her resentment of her condition. She is often discouraged, anxious, depressed and angry. The more obsessed she becomes, the worse she feels emotionally. Gayle is very bitter that this is happening to her and constantly tells everyone how unfair it is.

Gayle is driving her husband, children and friends away from her. She has many positives in her life, but she can't see them because she's so focused on wanting her situation to be different. Her refusal to accept her situation keeps her miserable and is making her life worse.

Anna is only a few years older than Gayle. I visited Anna when I was doing home visits early in my career to a very poor section of the city. Anna lived on the second floor of a two-family flat. I was told the entrance door was left open because Anna couldn't come down the stairs. Upon entering the flat, I couldn't find her. Anna called to me from a bedroom in the back. She was so severely crippled with rheumatoid

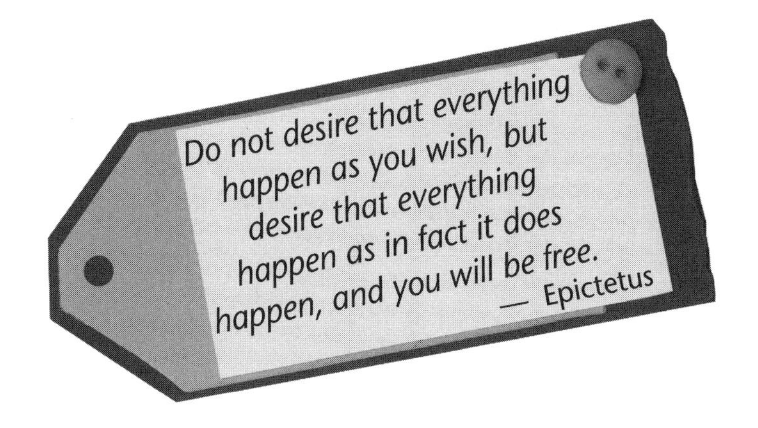

arthritis she was bedbound. Anna suffered from constant pain. She was left alone most of the day. Her granddaughter lived with her but worked weekdays. She had visiting nurses and neighbors check in on her periodically.

I expected to hear a barrage of complaints, all justified. Instead, Anna told me she had times she felt frustrated or down, but those feelings passed when she had a visitor or reflected on her many blessings. Anna proceeded to tell me how kind her granddaughter was to her and how fortunate she was to have so many people check on her and care about her. Anna said that she knew if she needed something or was too uncomfortable, that someone would come by, so she would wait. She admitted that she became impatient or angry sometimes but she knew it would pass, so she wasn't worried about it. Anna wouldn't think of moving to a nursing home. She was thankful for her situation and wanted to maintain it as long as possible.

Anna desired that everything happen just like it was and she was free. While Gayle, who seems to have so much going for her, resists what was happening and is imprisoned.

Choose to be like Anna.

When you experience chronic pain it's very easy to fall into a rut and adopt a negative outlook. When you personalize these negative feelings by fighting against them with self-hatred or complaints, they become further ingrained. It's easy to become full of self-pity. Nothing is fair or easy or enjoyable. This perspective further perpetuates undesirable thoughts and feelings. View your negative feelings as temporary, for that's what they can be.

Accepting your situation or feelings means it is what it is right now, not that you're not going to try and change it or improve the situation.

Exercise

1. Do you accept your health/chronic pain just as it is today? Remember, accepting it does not mean you don't wish to improve. If you don't accept your current status, you will remain stuck in that place. Acceptance allows you to move forward and make changes gracefully. Write down what you accept about your situation.

2. If you don't accept your health condition or chronic pain, do you know what your block is? Are you afraid accepting it means it won't improve? Can you believe this isn't true? It's just the opposite. Acceptance facilitates healing. What else keeps you from acceptance?

Set realistic goals. Most people heal slowly. Some people stabilize and don't progress further. Whatever your situation is, set reachable, realistic goals for your health. If you feel frustrated or are having trouble reaching your goal, set a more attainable goal. Be gentle with yourself; healing often occurs in small ways.

When you disregard your goal or attempt to deny your pain and engage in behavior, diet or activity that aggravates your condition, you are sabotaging yourself.

Sue was divorced with three grown children. She had a master's degree in nursing and had been able to support herself, until her multiple health problems became worse and worse. She was in and out of the hospital so many times she couldn't hold a job. She moved in with her mother and stepfather, going on disability.

Sue became very depressed and discouraged. Her mother and stepfather argued a lot. Her elderly grandmother also lived there and ruled everyone with her whims. If Sue needed a ride to the doctor the same time Grandma wanted to go to the Dollar Store, Grandma always came first.

Sue's chronic pain became worse. She had trouble sleeping and concentrating and went into a deep depression. She felt guilty that her mother was caring for everyone without support. When she would have a good day, she would cook a big dinner and mop floors, sending herself into a backslide with her pain. Her family told her if she could do things one day they didn't understand why she couldn't the next. She would try harder to appease them, and it became a vicious cycle.

Sue realized she had to make her own quality of life a priority. She called around to community resources and used supports that were available to her like van rides, counseling and financial assistance. She kept doctors appointments, arranged her own transportation and received counseling.

Sue asked her children to help with chores that were too much for her

> *Healing Help*
>
> Be aware of how everything you do has a ripple effect. If you think you can do something and it aggravates your condition, this affects your mood, outlook, energy and the intensity of pain. The effect is often immediate but may linger for days or longer. Don't disregard possible consequences. Be patient. Accept limitations while working to overcome them.

and her mother or stepfather to do, like yard work and heavy cleaning. When friends, neighbors or church members offered to do something, she started accepting. She made simpler meals a couple of times a week instead of a big dinner that exhausted her. For family parties and holidays, she had potluck dinners and bought sides and desserts instead of making them.

She started volunteering two half-days a week at a local nursing home. She made friends, enjoyed what she did and felt appreciated again.

Sue's health was stabilizing. Due to her pacing, support and improved outlook, she was out of her roller coaster cycle. She set a goal to move into her own apartment. Sue knew she could easily get caught up in wanting to move; it would be easy to overdo things again and restart her cycle. She had been running into numerous obstacles with her apartment goal. However, she continued to pace herself and do the things she knew she needed to do to maintain stability. Sue was committed to persevere in her goal. She knew her progress was about direction.

Each time you backslide, it's harder to regroup. No one is perfect, and you'll have times when you have contributed to a flare-up. Refocus. Are you being too rigid? Can you meet the goal you've set? Is it realistic? Is the goal achievable? Do you need to set a smaller goal? It feels good to reach a goal. It's frustrating to have a goal that is out of reach. Be fair to yourself. Set realistic goals.

Family Support

Families frequently overestimate or underestimate their loved one's functional ability. Both perspectives can be damaging. Resist the temptation to pigeon hole them.

Exercise

1. Review your goals. Are you making progress? If not, assess why. Is the goal too aggressive? What adjustments could be made to get back on track?

2. Do you have action steps outlined? Are they realistic? Remember, it's not all about good days. You have to factor in bad or off days, too. If your action steps aren't working, redo them at this time.

   ACTION STEPS:

Every day give yourself recognition for things you have accomplished. Don't analyze whether you did enough or should have done more. You did the best you could and that is good enough.

You paid a bill, even though it was hard to write the check. You complimented someone, even though your pain was bothering you. You wrote a long overdue letter, even if it was a short note. You got out of bed. You got out of bed by yourself.

One of my clients is developmentally disabled. He attends a workshop in a shelter. Every day he is proud of the work he has finished. He is always on the lookout to help others. He carries a neighbor's garbage can back to their house from the curb. He brings in the paper for a roommate. He knows he can only do "little things." He also knows these are accomplishments for him, and they are meaningful when done for others.

An accomplishment is an accomplishment. You can only measure the scope, difficulty and importance of that accomplishment. Don't minimize yourself. Focus on your accomplishments. Feel proud of what you can do.

Healing Help

Talk positively to yourself throughout the day. Tell yourself that you did a good job, give yourself encouragement, root for yourself.

Family Support

Recognize and compliment your loved one for his or her accomplishments. It feels good to hear it from others. I often tell clients that they are doing a good job of just making it through the day. They appreciate the recognition and know I understand their struggles.

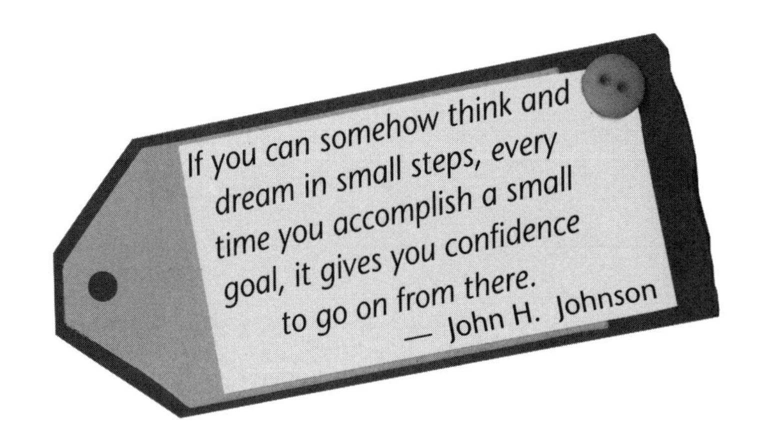

Exercise

List five things you are currently doing that you feel good about:

1. ______________________________
2. ______________________________
3. ______________________________
4. ______________________________
5. ______________________________

List five things that you like about yourself:

1. ______________________________
2. ______________________________
3. ______________________________
4. ______________________________
5. ______________________________

Healing Help

Being quiet is the best way to reconnect with your own judgement. Many people feel insecure and listen to others without taking the time to listen to themselves. Before you need to make a decision—take a walk by yourself, meditate, reflect and really listen to yourself.

Family Support

Many well-meaning family members believe they know what is best for their loved one when they really don't. The pressure to go against their own inner judgement in order to please family is stressful.

When you have an opinion about what your family member should do, practice empathy first. Really listen. Validate their feelings even if you don't agree with them. Their feelings are theirs. Respect their right to do what they feel is best. If you think there may be a backlash, set your own boundaries on how you will respond.

There are many traditional and alternative treatments available. How can you know what is best? Stay open minded. Do not automatically assume everything "alternative" is suspect or vice versa.

Be your own advocate. Research and rely on people you can trust. However, do not put all your trust in one person. Many doctors are not specifically trained in pain management and carry their own prejudice regarding treatments. Western medicine is wonderful for acute pain, but doesn't really understand most chronic pain.

If your doctor is not adequately managing your pain, seek out a physician who is board certified in pain management. If you are receiving services from physical, occupational or mental health therapists, check on their experience with and training in chronic pain. Do not let professionals make you feel that your situation isn't responding the right way or that you have a unique problem. Often, the professional or treatment may not be adequate for your needs or there is not enough knowledge available about how to effectively treat your condition. It is not you personally. The right connection has not been made.

Similarly, you can go on a wild goose chase with alternative treatments. Some people become evangelistic and believe that what helped them will help you. Their bodies may respond differently than yours will. Healing requires much guesswork and trial and error. Stay open. Don't become disappointed or give up. The answer may be around the next corner.

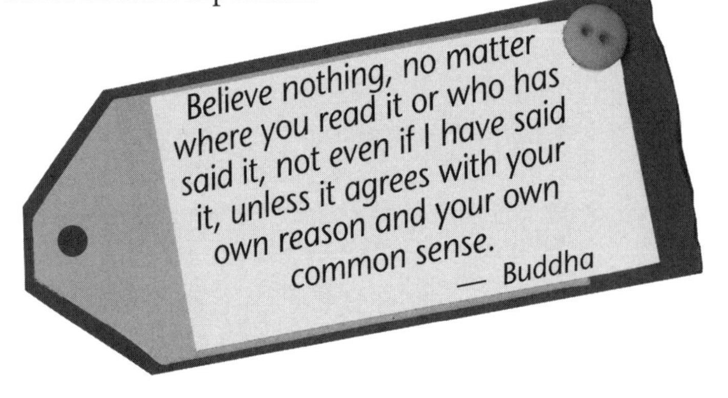

Exercise

Most people have an instinct about things. They may get "a feeling in their gut." How do you listen to your own judgement?

Where do you feel your instinct in your body? Is it in your gut, your heart, a feeling?

When you need to make a decision, quietly listen to your body and what it is telling you. Learn to listen to, trust and follow your own judgement. If you need to make a decision now, what is your judgement telling you to do:

For many people, it helps to list what separate parts of yourself are saying.

My fear is telling me ______

My anger is telling me ______

My emotions are telling me ______

My analytical mind is telling me ______

My ego is telling me ______

My inner wisdom is telling me ______

Simplify. That is a hot topic lately. There are books, magazines, and talk shows everywhere encouraging us to simplify our lives and really enjoy the everyday. There is much to be said for that.

How do we start? Follow your own instincts. Do not let yourself become overwhelmed with too much information. Read what appeals to you, take what seems to apply and put the rest aside. Some ideas may be good down the road, but not now.

Life is a process. Sometimes even simplifying has to be simplified. What is causing a lot of stress for you now? Start with priorities. You'll probably have to start with pieces of tasks initially.

One of the first things I started with was allowing more downtime for myself. I tried to underschedule myself at work and home. I have become better and better at this and my life has become not only more manageable, but much simpler and more enjoyable.

Instead of trying to simplify 10 different areas at once, start with one and give yourself all the time you need to accomplish the first area. You'll be amazed how this simple mindshift will allow the rest of your life to simply fall into place.

Healing Help

It's far more effective to focus on a few things than to feel overwhelmed. It doesn't matter what the area is or if you think you should be able to handle it. If it feels like too much, it is.

Family Support

Don't do too much for your loved one. If you feel overwhelmed, you are. It's not up to you to do everything. I'm always amazed how things resolve when someone says, "I can't do this any longer." Life always goes on. There are always other options. Take care of yourself and be sure you have simplified your life, too.

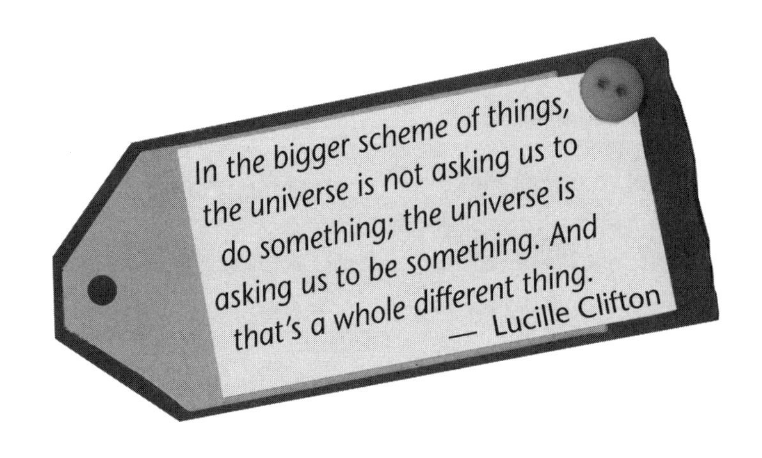

Exercise

1. Pick one area of your life to simplify. It can be projects at work, housework at home, volunteer involvement, anywhere you feel stressed.

___

___

___

2. What steps will you take to simplify this one area?

ACTION STEPS:

___

___

___

___

___

___

___

___

3. Once you have identified an area and decided how to simplify it, defend it. If someone asks you to go against your plan, simply say "no." People may find it beneficial to schedule exercise or meditation, as well as play time with children or alone time with a spouse. You can then turn down requests for your time by saying, "I'm already scheduled" and you're being truthful. Scheduling this way also ensures these activities happen and don't fall through the cracks with the busyness of life.

> **Healing Help**
> Anti-depressants and talk therapy combined are very effective. Ask for both.

> **Family Support**
> Many organizations have support groups for families. See the Resources section at the back of this book for listings. If you are depressed, seek treatment for yourself as well.

If you are so depressed your sadness is clouding your life, get help. If you are being treated for the physical pain but not the psychological issues, it is not enough.

If you are on an anti-depressant, talk to the doctor who prescribed it. Sometimes anti-depressants or related medications are prescribed at lower levels for sleep or other issues. There are so many kinds of medications. You might respond better to a different one. You may need a higher dose or a combination.

Speak up and let the right people know. Depression is curable. Be open to do what you need to feel better. Sometimes a support group, counseling or seeing a psychiatrist can help. Do not accept feeling depressed as a part of your pain. Treat depression. Don't be a martyr.

So many people tell me they expect depression because of their situation.

Let me share a story about Laura. Her children deserted her in a nursing home. They only lived a short distance away but never called. Her legs were so swollen with edema you could feel her pain by just looking at them. She was confined to bed most of the time. Various traditional and experimental treatments had failed. Laura was on anti-depressants but remained depressed.

I met with her once a week for a year. She processed through her grief and anger. She came to accept her situation without giving up hope. She became grateful for the staff who had "adopted her" by checking in on her constantly and even visiting on days off and holidays.

She appreciated being able to do mending for other residents and fondly reminisced about when she was a seamstress. She felt productive again. She accepted love and friendship from staff and other residents.

She remained hopeful that she would gradually improve, and she relied on her faith. She lived the same life without depression.

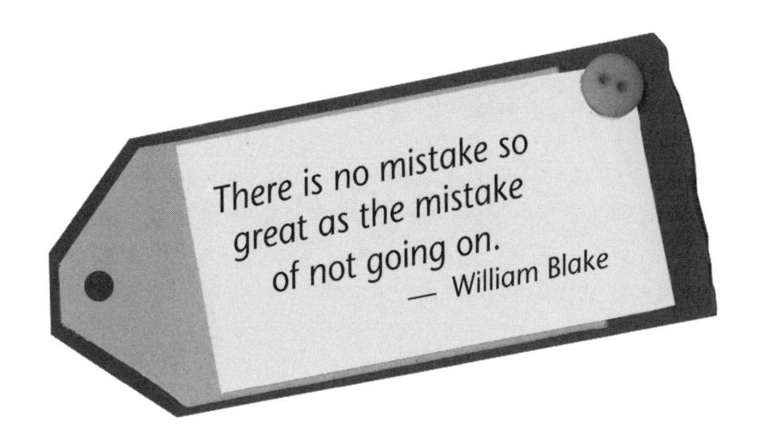

Exercise

Take this screening test for clinical depression by checking the boxes that apply to you:

- ❑ Feelings of sadness and/or irritability.
- ❑ Loss of interest or pleasure in activities you once enjoyed.
- ❑ Changes in weight or appetite.
- ❑ Feeling guilty.
- ❑ Inability to concentrate, remember things or make decisions.
- ❑ Fatigue or loss of energy.
- ❑ Restlessness or decreased activity noticed by others.
- ❑ Feeling hopeless or worthless.
- ❑ Thoughts of suicide or death.

If you checked fewer than five symptoms for the self-screening test, according to the National Mental Health Association, this determines that you are not suffering from severe clinical depression. However, checking even one or two of the above may indicate a type of depression. If it is causing you significant distress, go for a professional assessment.

If you checked five or more, you need to seek a qualified mental health professional for assessment and appropriate treatment. Ask your doctor, call your mental health association, call the association for people with your health / pain condition (i.e. fibromyalgia, M.S., chronic back pain). There is a very high correlation between chronic pain and depression. Don't wait.

Healing Help

You have everything that you need within you to cope with your current challenges. Draw from your past experience and use those lessons now.

Family Support

Encourage your loved one by reinforcing the strengths and skills that they already have.

Of all of the traits and gifts in my life, perseverance has been the most practiced. Through my many trials and tribulations, both personal and physical, I have relied on perseverance again and again.

My father was 100 percent Finnish. My dad told my sisters and me that because we were Finnish we were born with *sisu*. Sisu is a Finnish word that roughly translates to "the courage to persevere". He told us our great-grandmother became widowed with seven children when she was eight months pregnant and had no way to support herself and her children. She also took an orphan boy in. With children in tow, she boarded a train for a destination where farmland was inexpensive, but she didn't know anyone there and had never even visited the area.

She bought the farmhouse and land on a land contract deal. She worked with the boys in the field while one daughter took care of the house, cooking and the baby, once he was born. They made it! My great-grandmother and her kids had sisu.

There have been many days that I didn't know how I would make it. My hope seemed dim, my faith was weakening, and I didn't feel loved. But I have never doubted my sisu. I knew I would persevere. I would keep going, day after day, until my light finally looked brighter and my hope was restored. My prayers grew stronger, and my faith was full.

I loved myself and was open to receiving love from others. When all else seems to be failing, persevere. If you feel you can, you are now an honorary Finn. You have sisu. You have the courage to persevere.

Exercise

1. Think of times in your past when you have felt discouraged but you kept going. Write out what happened and what you did. What is the most significant memory?

2. Looking back at the experience in #1, what strengths or skills did you draw on (i.e. faith, support from family or friends, a strong conviction). Elaborate on your experience and how you implemented your strength(s) and skill(s).

3. What was the outcome of your experience? How did you feel about yourself afterward?

4. How can you use those same strengths or skills to help you now?

Healing Help

Face your fear and take action even though you are afraid. You'll emerge stronger.

One of the greatest obstacles we all face is fear. Fear of the unknown. Fear of the future. Fear of the present. We doubt if we will be able to cope day in and day out. We doubt our medical care. We doubt ourselves. We live in fear.

Fear immobilizes us. Fear does not keep us safe; it keeps us from moving forward. A recent counseling referral I met with stated she was so afraid. She was afraid to start counseling because she felt if she learned to accept and cope with her pain she might never be free of pain. Yet, she was afraid to live with the pain. Her pain consumed her life. She was afraid to go out for a ride because she might not enjoy it. She was locked in fear inside her house.

Alice is a very sweet elderly lady who recently faced her fear. She has chronic abdominal pain and trouble sleeping as a result. This was aggravated by a roommate who made loud noises all night. Alice desperately wanted to change rooms so she could sleep. Alice told the nurses her situation and received sympathy but no room change. She told the social worker and was shown a room she felt was worse, so she refused it. For months, Alice complained about her noisy roommate and not being able to sleep.

I asked Alice why she didn't take it to the next step and talk to the administrator. Alice said she was afraid. Initially, she didn't know what she was afraid of.

The first step in facing your fear is to clearly define it. After discussing it, Alice realized she was afraid the administrator didn't like her and would say no.

Once the fear is clearly identified, decide what possible action steps there are. One possibility is always to do nothing. Alice realized not taking action was making her miserable and that she needed to do something.

Making the commitment to do something means you're halfway there. Deciding "how to" is next. Alice had already tried talking to her roommate, the nurses and the social worker. She decided revisiting those efforts would not be productive. Alice made the commitment that the administrator needed to become involved. Alice analyzed the pros and cons of asking a nurse or trusted friend to go with her, contacting an ombudsman to represent her, writing a request or setting up a meeting herself. Looking at each option helped Alice decide she would obtain the best results by setting up a meeting herself, which she did. Analyzing the pros and cons, anticipating what's the worst that could happen as a result and deciding if she could accept and handle the possible outcomes led to the next step.

The next step is the last step. In order to face your fear, you have to implement the action step you've decided upon. You may still feel afraid, but you have thought it through, possibly received feedback from others and most importantly made the commitment. Just do it!

Alice met with the administrator who responded appropriately to her request at the initial meeting but did not move her. However, Alice was not afraid anymore. Alice regularly checked in with the administrator on room availability.

Alice faced her fear and increased her self-confidence as a result. She was no longer a passive victim, she was her own active advocate. If she didn't receive a room change with one approach, she would go through the process again. She overcame her fear and was confident to go on facing her fears until her goal was met.

The more fears you face the more empowered you become. Today, Alice is very content in a new room. Take the risk. Move past the fear. Do not be afraid to face fear.

Family Support

Sometimes, the chronic pain sufferer's fears seem silly to you. They may seem out of proportion, but remember that they are very real to your loved one.

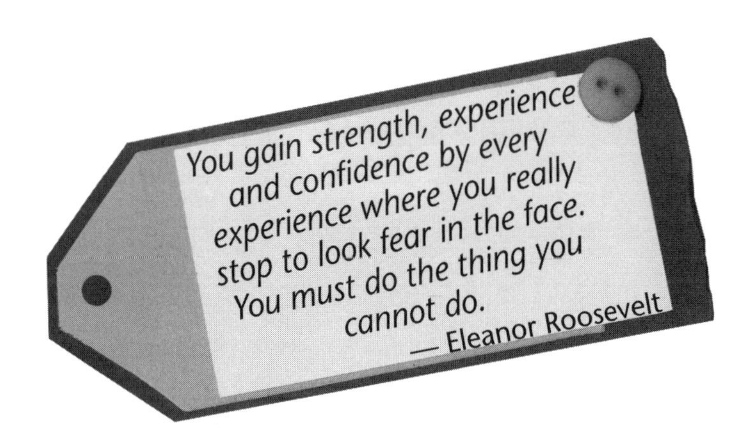

Exercise

1. What are you afraid of? Clearly define your fear.

2. What options or possible action steps can you take?

List the pros and cons of your top five options.

	Pros	Cons
1.		
2.		
3.		
4.		
5.		

3. After looking at your options and the pros and cons, are you able to commit to implementing one? Which one? When and how will you implement the step you committed to?

Love is patient, love is kind.
It does not envy, it does not boast, it is not proud.
It is not rude, it is not self seeking, it is not easily angered,
it keeps no record of wrongs. Love does not delight in evil
but rejoices with the truth. It always protects,
always trusts, always hopes, always perseveres.
Love never fails . . . And now these three remain:
faith, hope and love.
But the greatest of these is love.

— 1 Corinthians 13:4

Be compassionate for others as well as to yourself. Do not let yourself become so self-absorbed that you think your story is the only one worth telling. Even if you feel your pain is worse than another's, listen. Surrender your need for attention.

Everyone needs positive attention from other people. In order to have positive, giving friends, you need to be a positive (at least sometimes), giving friend.

If all you do is dominate conversations complaining about your pain, people will start to avoid you. If you don't listen, people will not want to listen to you.

There have been many times I have not mentioned any of my health or pain issues with a friend, until that friendship has become well developed. I save my need for attention for the times I really need it, with the friends I trust to give me what I need.

If I do talk about pain or health issues early in a relationship, it is usually to validate a person's comments. If they complain their back aches, I might say, "I understand, I have a similar problem with my neck."

Healing Help

The more support you give others, the less you focus on your own pain and problems. Be careful to balance your friendships with people who give and take support. It can become too draining to always give and never receive.

Family Support

Practice empathy for your loved one. This is the number one reason people see me for counseling when they are having chronic pain. They want empathy.

Exercise

Practice empathy by trying to understand what the other person is saying from their point of view and identifying their feelings. Empathy doesn't mean you agree with them, it means you understand their feelings. Empathy builds rapport and trust.

You can show empathy by paraphrasing, which is stating the other person's ideas in your own words and identifying their feelings. You can mirror what the other person said by simply repeating their words back.

An example of paraphrasing is, "I try to talk to my doctor about my pain, but he doesn't listen to me." An empathetic response would be: "You feel *upset* because *your doctor isn't responding to you.*"

Fill in the blanks below to practice paraphrasing.

"My pain pills don't help."

You feel ______________________________ because ____________________________.

"My husband/wife expects me to do more and I don't feel good."

You feel ______________________________ because ____________________________.

An example of mirroring is, "My back really hurts when I sit for a long time." An empathetic response would be, "Your back really hurts when you sit for a long time."

Fill in the blanks below to practice mirroring.

"My stomach hurts."

Your ____.

"I don't like needles or MRI's."

You ____.

Don't expect people to understand. Many times the people closest to us, who we wish understood us best, don't. Give up your need for validation. Let go of wanting approval or sanction for what you are trying to do.

If you know you need a nap, take one. You don't need anyone's approval. Live your life on your own terms. If you know a particular food aggravates a condition, don't eat it.

Doing things his own way is slowly transforming Todd's life. Todd is a 48-year-old single male. He lives in a nursing home due to a severe head injury. Todd also has severe chronic pain due to GERD. Todd has been spending most of his time in bed.

He has been hospitalized multiple times for extensive testing, and the doctors repeatedly have told him the pain is "primarily psychological." His pain medicine and anti-depressants have been constantly adjusted and changed, without good results. Todd has told everyone he feels "dismal."

His family has bought him a new computer to distract him. It has sat unused. The nurses have told him he should go to activities. Nothing interests him.

I started seeing Todd for counseling as a last resort. No one believed it would help. Todd frequently complained to me that no one understood or believed him. I validated his feelings and reinforced his ability to be understanding to himself. I encouraged him to decide how to approach his situation.

Todd has now started his own exercise routine in bed. He is very disciplined about doing it twice a day. Todd has set a goal of being able to walk in two years. (His leg muscles atrophied from not using them and damage from his injuries.) Now when I talk with Todd, he sits up and smiles. He goes outside on nice days. He is positive.

Todd has taken responsibility to do what he feels is best. He still has chronic pain, he still lives in a nursing home, and others still don't believe him. But Todd now believes in himself.

Take responsibility for your life and your health. Do what you believe is best to take care of yourself. Don't expect people to understand. Understand yourself.

Healing Help

The more you set and enforce appropriate boundaries, the more self-confident you become. Practice makes it easier each time.

Family Support

Families often have difficulty respecting boundaries. It can seem obvious to you that your loved one has self-defeating behavior that aggravates their pain or options they could choose to improve their situation. It can be painful to watch your loved one make poor decisions, but that's how they learn and grow. If you push your opinions, it frequently creates barriers.

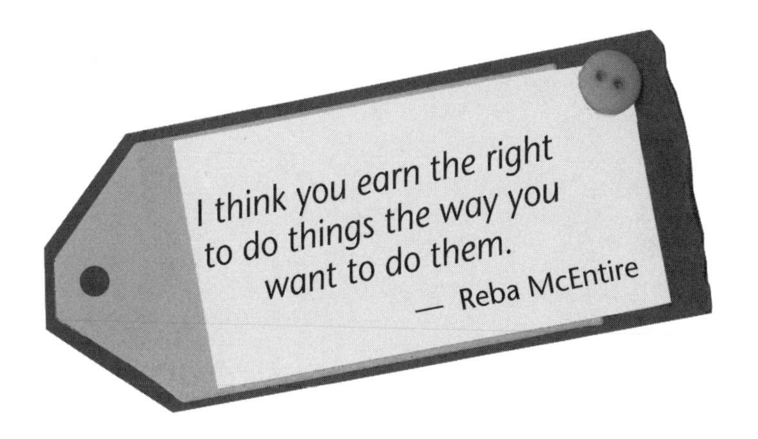

Exercise

Many times people with chronic pain have blurry boundaries, meaning they lack faith in their own judgement and allow others to direct them, often inappropriately. It's important to have faith in your own judgement and confidence in yourself and your feelings in order to make knowledgeable decisions that are in your best interest. No one else can fully understand what you are going through. It's wise to have trusted advisors, gather accurate information and then be responsible for your own consequences. Are you able to clearly define what decisions are appropriate for you to make on your own? List some of your decisions regarding your health.

____

____

____

If you are having problems with boundary issues, start with one person or issue. Use the goal setting steps to clarify what you want. Are you clear regarding what you want? Map out small steps that will lead to what you desire. (Refer to "Be Patient" on pages 38 and 39 for a refresher.)

ACTION STEPS:

____

____

____

____

____

____

When someone tries to influence you on that particular issue, you will have a clear response. If the person pushes and you feel they are not respecting your boundaries or response, stay strong and clear in enforcing them. It's easy for boundaries to become blurry when you aren't sure where you stand. The more clear you are in your own mind, the more clearly you can communicate and enforce your own decisions.

Get enough sleep. Many of us are sleep deprived. Time management books tell us to wake up an hour earlier in order to accomplish more. I say in order to feel better, get enough sleep.

I typically feel best on eight to 10 hours of sleep per night. I often lay down for half an hour or an hour in the afternoon on top of that. I have chosen to honor my body and when it tells me I need to rest, I do my best to rest. I find I am more effective and functional overall if I take the time when I need it.

If you are not sleeping well at night, try different approaches. I used to meditate for one to two hours before I could fall asleep. I bought a hot tub to soak in and relax. I have tried reading in bed. As much as possible, follow a nightly routine to train your body.

Not sleeping is very stressful. When this happens don't fight it. That makes it worse. Try to distract yourself by watching a movie or boring TV show. I like to lay quietly with all of the lights out and daydream. Sometimes I daydream for an hour or so, but at some point my daydream becomes my sleeping dream. I wake up very easily, like many pain sufferers who have a hard time going into a deep sleep.

I have taught my children to whisper in the house and to be quiet when I am sleeping. Talk to your doctor. Muscle relaxers for spasms, sleeping pills, anti-depressants and some herbs are all helpful options during difficult times.

I will never forget an Alzheimer's patient support group that I was leading several years ago. Many of the participants were in the middle stage. They enjoyed the conversation but needed to keep it very simple. We were going around the circle giving suggestions on how to deal with a bad day. Many people were rambling and did not make a lot of sense. When we came to one of the most confused women she stated, "Take a nap!" Her wisdom still rings true.

When I feel badly, am crabby or overwhelmed, I've found that often what I need is a nap. Next time life is too much, try a nap and see if you just needed some sleep.

Healing Help

Comfortable, soft clean sheets are important, too. Wash them regularly. Also, just the right sleepwear can make a difference. I love to take a hot bath, use clean soft towels to dry off, put on clean soft p.j.s and climb into clean, soft sheets with a comforter. Make sure the room temperature is just right and that your covers are keeping you warm enough or cool enough.

Family Support

Are you getting enough sleep? It's said that 40 percent of Americans are sleep deprived. It's a problem that affects many of us. Are you doing everything you can to get a good night's sleep?

Exercise

Are you making a good night's sleep a priority? What does your bedroom look like? Feel like? Do you enjoy being in your bedroom? Do you like the way it's decorated? The décor, is it clean or cluttered? Is the lighting the way you need it to be? Is it noisy at night or quiet? Is your bed comfortable? What time do you need to go to bed in order to get enough sleep? What gets in the way of doing this?

If you are having issues with any of these questions, start working on correcting them. If it's overwhelming, prioritize and start small. Sleep is very important. Your bedroom needs to be a high priority, not an afterthought. List solutions.

If you are not able to resolve your sleep problems on your own, talk to your doctor. There are some mild options available to aid with sleep that can be increased or decreased as needed. However, don't let a pill be your total solution. Make appropriate modifications to benefit yourself, too. You need to sleep!

No matter how bad you feel there are people who feel worse, people in more pain, who are more disabled, in less fortunate circumstances, who have less support and fewer resources. No matter what your situation is, find a way to reach out to someone else.

I know a woman named Nancy with a severe neurological disorder who is homebound. However, she makes phone calls to shut-ins; she also sends sympathy cards to hospice families.

Nancy told me, "I know they can't read my writing, but it's the thought that counts, and I hope they are comforted by the card and the effort."

An elderly man, so severely paraplegic that he can barely move his own wheelchair, gingerly pushes other residents to and from their nursing home dining room. He is slow, but for him, it is better than just sitting. Many people he helps are more physically capable than he is. He always has a smile on his face when he is helping someone.

No matter how severe my pain has been, when I know someone needy is counting on me, I can pull myself together. Afterwards, even if I am not physically feeling better, my soul is singing.

No matter how bad your own pain is, put it aside once in a while and give to someone in need. You'll both feel better.

Healing Help

Be a volunteer! If you don't know how to get started, contact your local library. They should have listings of non-profit agencies in your area. Decide what interests you and start calling. Everyone loves and needs volunteers.

Family Support

Support your loved one's volunteer efforts. It's good for them to be needed and giving. If you want them to do more around the house, don't make it an either/or scenario. Often, people increase their energy for something they look forward to or feel appreciated doing. Volunteering can be a key part of healing.

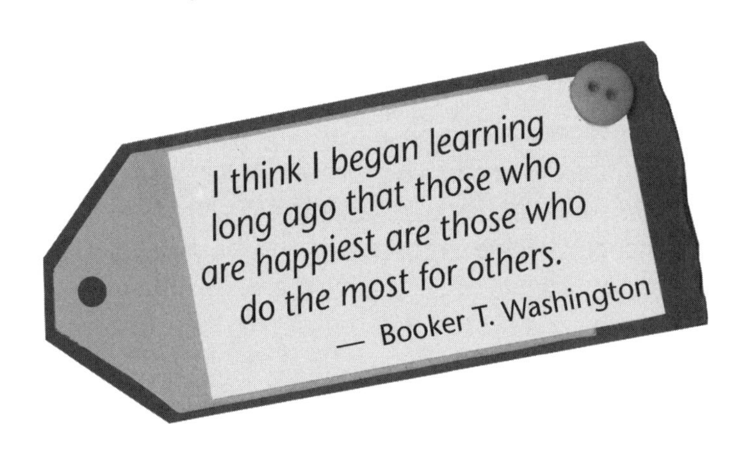

How do you think of others?

Do you volunteer or practice random acts of kindness? If so, how? If not, how could you?

Make giving to others a regular part of your schedule. Whether it's through a formal organization or putting change in a parking meter — incorporate a system and time in your schedule. Once you're in the habit, you'll wonder why you didn't do it before. Everyone has something to offer. It really makes *you* feel better.

Be very particular about whom you spend time with. Surround yourself with loving, supportive, positive people.

People who are negative, demanding or just plain mean are toxic. They are toxic not only to your physical health, but also to your mental health and to your soul.

This is easier than it sounds. Once I started eliminating toxic people from my circle, I also started bringing more positive people into my life. I was careful to stop relationships when I realized someone was toxic to me.

The hardest decision for me was to divorce my first husband. Amazingly, soon after the divorce my life really started to come together. I made good decisions; I received better and more effective treatments; my overall quality of life improved and my pain started decreasing.

Surround yourself with positive people as much as you can. Be a positive, supportive person for others. I promise this one decision will change your life more than you can imagine.

Healing Help

To meet more healthy people, join groups where healthy people are already gathering. Women's organizations, health/community agencies, religious settings. Try something completely different. I met my second husband at a Rotary Club. I would have never attended one before, but I was expanding my horizon of healthy people.

Family Support

Encourage your loved one to try new groups. Don't let their diagnosis limit their settings.

Exercise

List the positive people in your life:

List the negative/toxic people in your life:

How can you increase time with positive people and decrease or eliminate negative people from your life? Are there places you could go, boundaries you could set, time not spent any more with certain people?

This is your life. Do not sit by passively waiting for someone to give you the answers you want. No one cares as much as you should. If you are not getting effective treatments or you are being treated in a condescending manner—stand up for yourself.

You need caring, empathetic doctors and other professionals. Try talking to people about what you expect from them and what your goals are. Make sure you are clear about your expectations. Realistically, can you work to have your pain go down two points on the pain scale?

Write out questions and request information on conditions and treatments before you go in. Make a copy for your doctor and have the receptionist put it on the front of your chart or hand it to the doctor when he or she walks in. Keep your own copy. Go over it together.

If your pain medicine is not adequate, advocate for what you need. The average doctor will under-medicate or incorrectly medicate pain. Many doctors are reluctant to medicate what they can't see. Most chronic pain is not visible on an X-ray.

That doesn't mean it's not there or that the sufferer is exaggerating. I have worked with many clients referred to me by their doctors for exaggerating their pain. I haven't worked with one person I haven't believed.

Figure out your own insurance coverage and requirements. Do not expect your doctor or his office to know what your policy covers. If something is not covered and you believe you need it, be willing to pay for it out of pocket. It's your life. No one cares as much as you do.

Healing Help

When I had a lot of pain issues at one time, I would write up a summary before my appointment. When you're in pain, it can be hard to concentrate and easy to feel confused, especially if you feel rushed. So many clients tell me they forget to mention concerns. Writing the overview with specific concerns/questions ensures your time meets your needs.

Family Support

Depending on the severity and complexity of your loved one's pain, they may benefit from your help with their medical file. There were so many times I would have appreciated a family advocate. Talk to your loved one about it.

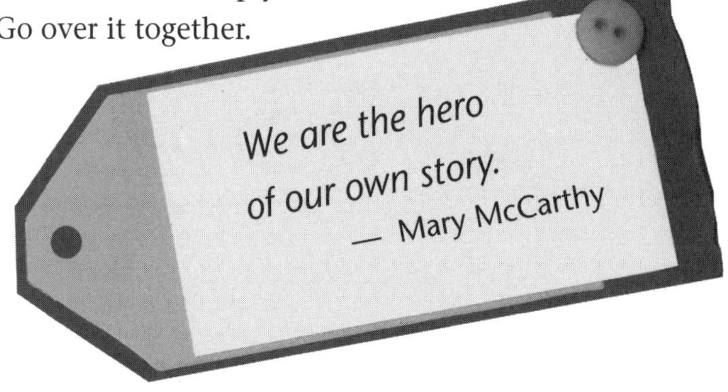

Keep a file on yourself. Every time you go to a doctor, have questions written out—after you talk with the doctor, write in the answers. Be sure it's dated and file it. Keep all your medications and treatments documented in this file. Carry it with you to appointments. Keep a bag just for this file.

You don't have to be an organized person to do this. It will make a big difference. Specialists, primary doctors, allied health professionals and alternative providers don't communicate. I've read two physicians notes side by side in a hospital chart where it's obvious they don't read each others notes or talk to each other.

If you can tell each of them a correct history, current status, medications and other treatments and relevant updates, you will receive better care.

Well meaning people may tell you that you have no right to feel sorry for yourself. You should be putting on a brighter face to the world. You could be doing better than you are if you would change your attitude.

Your feelings are yours. Do not let others attempt to manipulate your feelings. Yes, it helps to be optimistic when you can. Often, this requires a process of feelings where you are sad and/or angry first. Even when you have processed through issues, there will be more issues to sort through and days that aren't so good.

A lady with chronic pelvic pain told me everyone criticized her because her granddaughter has cerebral palsy. They would say to her, "How could you even think of your pain when this little girl has such a burden to carry?"

Your life is yours. You can't compare how you should feel. Denying your situation keeps you from accepting it.

When you accept your pain, you can be free from its chains.

Healing Help

You don't have to defend yourself when you are being questioned. If it's a self-care decision, saying you feel it's appropriate is enough.

Family Support

Practice accepting your loved one and yourself. Be sure you have healthy boundaries in place.

In order to reach acceptance, you must grieve the loss of the life you had and/or wanted. There are many theories about grieving. The most well known is from Elizabeth Kubler-Ross' book, *On Death and Dying*. Even though her work was devoted to people who were dying, it's now felt these stages apply to all types of grieving. They are:

1. Denial — "This isn't happening to me!"

2. Anger — "Why is this happening to me?"

3. Bargaining — "I promise to be a better person if…"

4. Depression — "I don't care anymore."

5. Acceptance — "I am ready for whatever comes."

Not everyone goes through every stage or in this exact order, but it's a very good guideline. It's also likely that over the course of time, stages will be revisited at different or deeper levels. It's an on-going process.

Can you identify at what stage you are now? How does this feel? Describe your emotions.

____

____

____

____

____

____

Give yourself time and permission to grieve. When you are ready, take responsibility for things you have control over and surrender the rest. Practicing acceptance means that you accept yourself, others and circumstances just as they are. Practice acceptance by telling yourself through self-talk and affirmations what you are working on accepting; say that you already accept it. If someone tells you they don't accept you or something about you, don't argue with them. It's their issue, not yours.

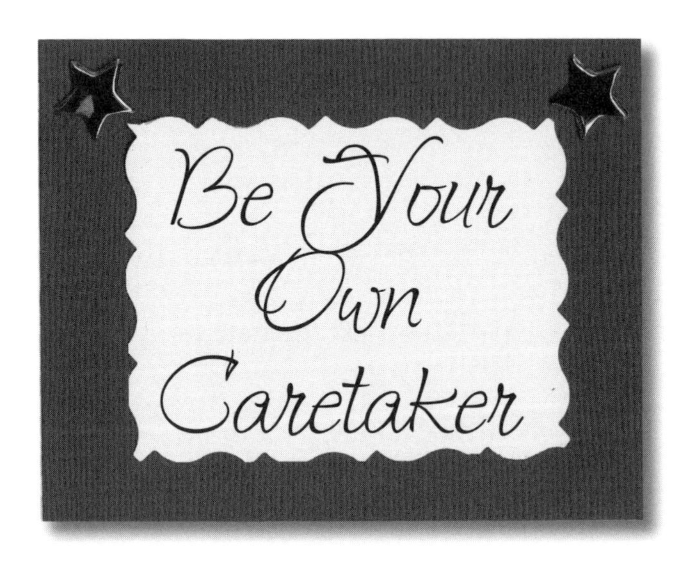

Be gentle with yourself. Treat yourself as you would treat your mother, child or best friend. Give yourself all the compassion and understanding that you need. Love yourself, with all your imperfections, with all of your pain.

Pain is not a punishment. Pain does not mean you are less worthy than other people without pain. Everyone has something to bear. Some people may seem to be problem-free, but no one has it made. Life is not always easy. We have to work at making our life good for ourselves.

Unnecessary demands or expectations increase our stress and pain. Criticism and self-pity make each day harder. Feel warmth and kindness toward yourself. Soften your heart. Ease up on your anger and perfectionism.

Balinda works as a caregiver for the elderly. I have referred several clients to her over the years because she is so good. Balinda is very kind and hardworking.

Over time, I have come to know Balinda pretty well. I found out she suffers from chronic back pain, which is frequently aggravated when she is transferring people. Once I found that out, I arranged to have needed equipment in place and at times another caregiver to work with her. I started pestering Balinda to wear a back support and to let others know she couldn't do certain tasks. Balinda would complain and say she didn't want special treatment.

Balinda made it clear, she felt unworthy. She worked through meals, wore old clothes and never

Healing Help
Schedule what you need. No excuses. No guilt.

Family Support
Are you taking care of yourself? Be a role model as a caregiver by meeting your own needs first.

let herself have any fun. She was divorced and lived with her daughter and her family. Although only 50, she often said her life was behind her and her goal now was to help her grandchildren.

Balinda said it was not worth the time and effort it would take to see a doctor or to even soak in the tub. She frequently said she didn't need anything and didn't like frills like getting her hair done.

The client she was caring for died, and I lost contact with her for about a year. When I ran into her, I was surprised by the change. "You were right!" she shouted, with a huge smile. Her hair and nails were done and she was wearing new clothes. She was dating, going out and having fun. Her health was stable. She now sees a doctor regularly and her pain is under good control. She still works as a caregiver, but lets people know up front what her limitations are. She is pleased most people are supportive.

"I am worth it," she told me with a wink. The caregiver was finally taking care of herself.

Do not expect more of yourself than what you can do. Appreciate your many good qualities. Work on aspects of yourself that you want to change, but if you fall short or make a mistake, forgive yourself. I have seen many people treat their dogs better than they treat themselves. Today, be gentle with yourself.

Exercise

Once I accepted that I "need more" than many people to feel good, I thrived. Check the needs that apply for you. I need:

- ❑ More down time
- ❑ More fun
- ❑ More play
- ❑ More massages
- ❑ More alternative treatments
- ❑ More whirlpool baths
- ❑ More kind words
- ❑ More quiet
- ❑ More quality meals
- ❑ More time to exercise and stretch
- ❑ More meditation/prayer
- ❑ More love

Once I started meeting my own needs, though they seemed excessive to me, I became healthier and more giving. I no longer feel they are excessive; they are simply what I need. What do you need to do to take better care of yourself?

____

____

Listen to music whenever you can, but especially when you are feeling sad or negative. Music distracts you from your pain. Music lifts your spirits and can feed your soul. Music can break a pattern of negative obsessive thoughts.

Be sure to listen to music that is uplifting when you need a brighter outlook. I enjoy many styles of music, but I find I turn most to upbeat rock and roll when I am in a negative mood. I may listen to one uplifting song many times in a row.

Find the kind of music that makes you feel like singing and listen to it often. Sing along, and even dance if you can.

Be attuned to what you need from music at a given time. Make the attempt to listen to what your body, mind and soul desire to hear. Sometimes almost any music is satisfying; other times specific needs will only respond to specific music.

Be good to yourself with music.

Healing Help

Have times where you are quiet (in the car, making dinner, at work) and times you incorporate music. You'll appreciate the music more if it's not always present.

Family Support

If your loved one is confined to bed or physically disabled, be sure they have quality sound from a radio, CD player or tapes. Be sure they can operate it themselves and have a good selection of music they enjoy.

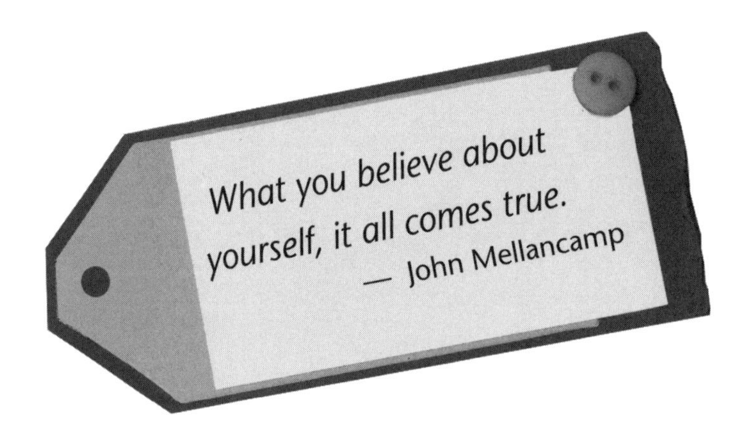

Exercise

What music do you listen to? Take time to incorporate uplifting music into your routine. Listen to the lyrics; keep it positive. Experiment with different stations, you may broaden your horizons and lift your spirits at the same time.

Give yourself a special reward every day, a gift of love to yourself. What makes you feel loved and healthier? Quiet time alone, sunshine, chocolate, being with a group of family or friends, a good book, cuddling with a pet or a child, a soothing bath, scented candles, your favorite movie?

You are lovable and you deserve love. You are making it through each day the best that you can. Appreciate yourself.

When you give yourself a special reward, tell yourself you are giving this special recognition to yourself because you are proud of something you did; you are worthy because you are you; give whatever is meaningful to you from you.

One of the most medically complicated cases I've had was an elderly lady with a rare neurological disorder. There was no cure. She had severe difficulty walking and was in a great deal of constant pain. She had a sharp mind. Her husband had Alzheimer's Disease. In this situation, you would think she might have given up.

Instead she honored herself with self-love. She went out for a weekly manicure. She kept in touch with friends. She attended the symphony even though the effort was monumental. She spent time on her appearance. She indulged in a favorite treat once in a while. No matter how dismal her situation and her husband's became, she rewarded herself daily because she knew she was worthy.

Vary what you do to keep it special. Remember you are special. Give yourself a gift of love.

Healing Help

Be sure you schedule something positive to reward yourself every day. Something you look forward to. It can be small or big. Vary it. Do something meaningful for you. Write it down on your calendar until it becomes a habit.

Family Support

Give a reward to your loved one on a regular basis. A note of encouragement, a special treat, a compliment. Support them in seeing their own value.

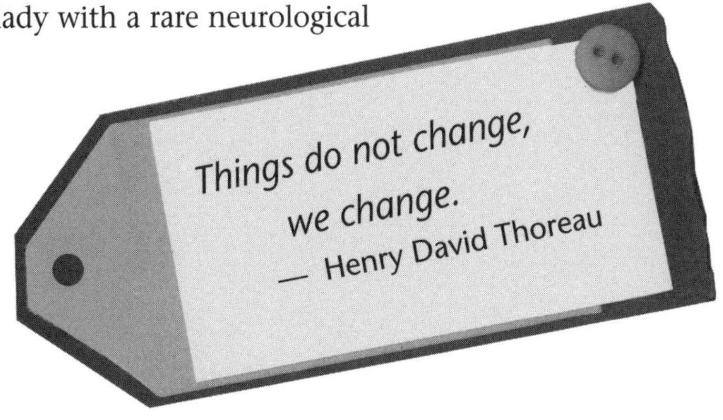

Exercise

Imagine you are talking to good friends who happen to be in a situation similar to yours. Write down what suggestions you would give them, so that every day is special for them (i.e., hire a sitter once a week/month and take the afternoon off, join a knitting group, accept help with a project).

____

____

____

____

____

____

Will you be a friend to yourself? What will you do?

____

____

____

I know you hurt. I know life is hard. I know you don't feel like it, but SMILE!

At first it will be forced and feel artificial. Make yourself consciously smile anyway. Fake it till you make it!

Smile at yourself in the mirror. You are a wonderful person — you deserve a smile. Smile at your family and friends. You appreciate them.

Smile at the receptionist in your doctor's office; she has to deal with a lot of crabby people. Your smile could make a difference.

When you smile you trick your brain into thinking you are happy. When you smile, people smile back at you. People respond more positively to you. When others smile at you, you feel better about yourself.

You will start to feel better inside when you smile.

Healing Help

Make it a point to smile at people who really need it—a nursing home resident, people at a soup kitchen, people in pain at a support group. They really appreciate your smile, and it feels good to smile.

Family Support

Smile at your loved one. People instinctively respond to a smile with a smile.

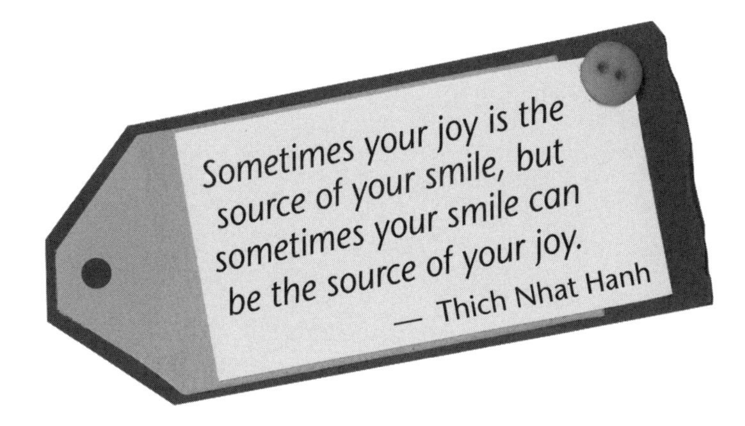

Exercise

Practice smiling. When you're in pain, you are frowning or scowling and may not even realize it. Force yourself to smile at yourself in the mirror. Write yourself reminders to smile in public. After a while it will become natural.

Healing Help

If you cannot identify your needs in the following exercises or aren't meeting them, it will be hard to heal. You have to feel a sense of comfort in every area or it will affect your health/pain.

Family Support

Encourage and support your loved one to meet their needs in all areas. Only focusing on one distracts from the others and results in a negative effect.

The greatest lesson I have learned through my journey called life thus far is to love myself. When I love myself I am truly honoring God. When I take care of myself, I am not being selfish, I am developing a healthier way to live.

When I put myself first, I am setting a good example for my children. I am teaching how to set boundaries, self-respect and healthy options.

Putting myself first does not mean I do not help others. It means I decide when it is right, good and appropriate to give. I give to my children, my family and my friends. I give to my church and my community. I am not worn thin, used or drained emotionally, physically or financially.

I make sure I am replenished before I give too much. I take responsibility for meeting my own emotional, health and financial needs.

I do not feel guilty that what I need may be different than what other people need. What may seem like pampering to others may be a need for me. If others don't understand, that is their issue, not mine.

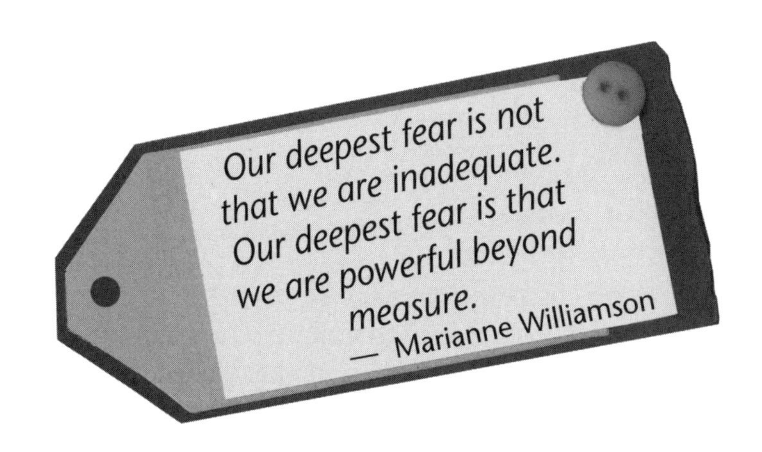

Exercise

What are your health needs?

What are you doing to meet them?

What are your emotional needs?

What are you doing to meet them?

What are your financial needs?

What are you doing to meet them?

What are your spiritual needs?

What are you doing to meet them?

Sometimes all that may be needed
to salvage the soul
and mend the heart
is a kind word
and a message of hope
and inspiration.

— *Yitta Halberstrom & Judith Leventhal*

First, learn everything you can about your loved one's medical condition. It is easy to dismiss conditions that are not understood. Go to Web sites and read books on the specific illness, the symptoms and manifestations and the treatment options. Understanding the exact nature of the diagnosis enables people to be more compassionate.

If your loved one does not have a diagnosis, help them find one. For 10 years my jaw would lock open or shut while I was eating. I had myofacial pain as well. Several doctors and dentists told me it was just in my head. The diagnosis of TMJ had not been medically accepted yet. There was a diagnosis for my problem, but it took over 10 years to find it. Doing my own research, I discovered this was the problem and identified a specialist in this area.

Many times the person with chronic pain does not have the energy to do the research and locate the appropriate provider. Ask them if you can help. Keep them updated and informed. Share your findings. It is very important for everyone to have good information.

Ask if you can go to the doctor or practitioner with your loved one. When a person is hurting, it's hard to keep track of everything. People often benefit from an advocate. Ask questions, take notes, and listen to what is being said. Be proactive; learn about various treatment options and explore their efficacy.

Be prepared to seek out a second or third opinion. Find out about pain management doctors and clinics offering pain treatments. Research alternatives and stay open yourself to various possibilities.

Be as patient as possible with your loved one. They may become frustrated and so will you. Be a supportive listener, but do not allow yourself to be worn down. Take care of yourself or you will not be able to help your loved one. Suggest that your loved one attend support groups or receive counseling if they need more support than you can give in a healthy relationship. You may need to attend a support group for families or receive counseling for yourself as well. Setting boundaries is good for both of you.

Touch. A soft stroke, hugs, kisses—whatever is loving and appropriate for the relationship can be healing. Many people are longing for a loving touch.

Encourage hope. Support faith. Help them to persevere. Love them. Love yourself. You are doing the best that you can. You cannot save someone from his or her pain. But your relationship can provide support for healing.

Pray for grace—for yourself and your loved one.

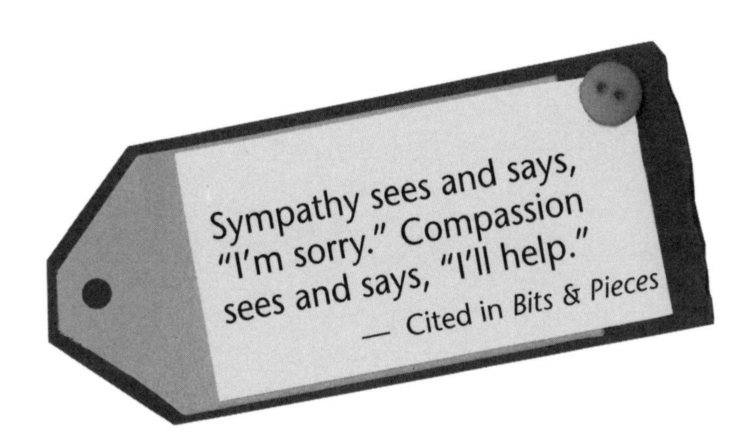

... to superintend to the sick
to make them well,
to care for the healthy
to keep them well,
also to care for one's own self.

— *Part of the Hippocratic Oath*

CHRONIC PAIN

American Academy of Pain Medicine
4700 W. Lake
Glenview, IL 60025
(847) 375-4731
www.painmed.org

American Alliance of Cancer Pain Initiatives
Serves the Ntl. Network of State Pain Initiatives; check your own state for a Pain Initiative
(608) 262-0978
www.aacpi.wisc.edu

American Chronic Pain Association
P.O. Box 850
Rocklin, CA 95677
www.theacpa.org

American Holistic Health Association
P.O. Box 17400
Anaheim, CA 92817
(714) 779-6152
www.ahha.org

American Pain Foundation
201 N. Charles St., Suite 710
Baltimore, MD 21201-4111
(888) 615-PAIN (7246)
www.painfoundation.org

Institute for Noetic Services
101 San Antonio Rd.
Petaluma, CA 94952
(707) 775-3500
www.noetic.org

The Mind-Body Medical Institute
110 Francis St., Suite 1A
Boston, MA 02215
(617) 632-7000
www.mbmi.org

American Pain Society
4700 W. Lake Ave.
Glenview, IL 60025
(847) 375-4715
www.ampainsoc.org

National Health Information Center
P.O. Box 1133
Washington, DC 20013-1133
(800) 336-4797
www.health.gov/NHIC

Preventative Medicine Research Institute
Dean Ornish, M.D.
900 Brideway, Ste. 2
Sausalito, CA 94965
(415) 332-2525
www.pmri.org

Web MD
www.WebMD.com
Provides medical information

CO-DEPENDENCY

Co-Dependents Anonymous
P.O. Box 33577
Phoenix, AZ 85067
www.codependents.org

DOMESTIC VIOLENCE

National Coalition Against Domestic Violence
P.O. Box 18749
Denver, CO 80218
(303) 839-1852
www.ncadv.org

National Domestic Violence Hotline
P.O. Box 161810
Austin, TX 78716
(800) 799-SAFE (24-hour hotline)
(800) 787-3224 (TTY)
www.ndvh.org

MENTAL HEALTH

American Psychiatric Association of America
1400 K St. NW
Washington, DC 20005
(888) 357-7924
www.psych.org

Anxiety Disorders Association of America
11900 Parklawn Dr., Ste. 100
Rockville, MD 20852
(240) 485-1001
www.adaa.org

The Help Center of the American Psychological Association
(800) 964-2000
www.helping.apa.org

The International Society of Mental Health Online
www.ismho.org

Knowledge Exchange Network
www.mentalhealth.org

National Center for Post-Traumatic Stress Disorder (PTSD)
(802) 296-5132
www.neptsd.org

National Alliance for the Mentally Ill
2107 Wilson Blvd., Ste. 300
Arlington, VA 22201
(800) 950-6264
www.nami.org

National Association of Social Workers
750 First St. N.E., Ste. 700
Washington, DC 20002
(202) 408-8600
www.naswdc.org

National Depressive and Manic-Depressive Association
730 N. Franklin St., Ste. 501
Chicago, IL 60610
(800) 826-3632
www.ndmda.org

National Institute of Mental Health
6001 Executive Blvd., Room 8184
MSC 9663
Bethesda, MD 20892
(301) 443-4513
(301) 443-8431 (TTY)
www.nimh.nih.gov

SUICIDE PREVENTION

Suicide Awareness Voices of Education (SAVE)
Minneapolis, MN 55424
(952) 946-7998

Suicide National Hotline
(800) 784-2433

SUPPORT GROUPS

To find a support group in your area for your specific health condition, check with local hospitals (ask for the social work department) or your local library for listings. Also check with a related association for your diagnosis.

www.supportpath.com
Leads you to thousands of resources for over 300 health and personal issues.

The Well Spouse Foundation
63 W. Main St., Ste. H
Freehold, NJ 07728
(800) 838-0879
www.wellspouse.org

National Family Caregivers Association (NFCA)
10400 Connecticut Ave., Ste. 500
Keningston, MD 20895-3944
(800) 896-3650
www.nfcacares.org

RECOMMENDED READINGS

RECOMMENDED READINGS

These are some of the books I have found to be most helpful.

Beyond Codependency: And getting better all the time, by Melody Beattie

Codependent No More: How to stop controlling others and start caring for yourself, by Melody Beattie

Don't Sweat the Small Stuff... And it's all small stuff, by Richard Carlson, Ph.D.

Heal Your Body, by Louise L. Hay

You Can Heal Your Life, by Louise L. Hay

Meditations to Heal Your Life, by Louise L. Hay

Law of Attraction, by Michael J. Loser

Love, Medicine & Miracles, by Bernie S. Siegel, M.D.

Oh, the Places You'll Go, by Dr. Seuss

POWER Optimism: Enjoy the Life You Have, Create the Success You Want, by Dana Lightman, Ph.D.

Simple Abundance: A daybook of comfort and joy, by Sarah Ban Breathnach

Simplify Your Life, by Elaine St. James

Taming the Tiger Within: Meditations on transforming difficult emotions, by Thich Nhat Hanh

The 7 Habits of Highly Effective People: Powerful lessons in personal change, by Stephen R. Covey

The Seven Spiritual Laws of Success, by Deepak Chopra

When Bad Things Happen to Good People, by Harold S. Kushner

Who Moved My Cheese?, by Spencer Johnson, M.D.

Additional Resources Online

For more helpful resources, to sign up for the Beyond Chronic Pain e-Newsletter, and to send in your own tips and stories, visit:

www.BeyondChronicPain.com